Lettie Hamlett Rogers

*To my mother
and to the memory of
my father*

LIBRARY OF CONGRESS CATALOG CARD NUMBER: 57-5678
MANUFACTURED IN THE UNITED STATES OF AMERICA
BY H. WOLFF, NEW YORK
DESIGN: *Marshall Lee*

Birthright

by Lettie Hamlett Rogers

SIMON AND SCHUSTER   NEW YORK

1957

South of Heaven
The Storm Cloud
Landscape of the Heart

For my book, I have taken the liberty of borrowing a constellation of family names (that is to say, surnames) from Burke County, North Carolina. I ask these families to forgive me, inasmuch as I do not know them, and everything I have attached to their names I have taken from elsewhere, mainly from that land of the imagination where the novelist dwells willy-nilly, for better or for worse. I had to have a certain constellation of what Proust calls "place names," because I did not know how to invent them. I have invented nearly everything else, including "the place" (although, of course, not "the time," any more than the generally shaping circumstances).

L. H. R.

PART ONE

Out of the mouth of babes and sucklings
hast thou ordained strength because of thine enemies,
that thou mightest still
the enemy and the avenger.

Martha Lyerly

1

DROPPING THE NEWSPAPER TO THE FLOOR, SHE WATCHED IT take the shape of an unstable pyramid or a tent in a state of collapse. She sat on the bed, perfectly still, not looking up from the paper, so that her eyes became set in their gaze and sightless. Her dark luxurious hair was untidy, the color was high in her cheeks; her mouth, a little too beautiful to be real, was rigid. She was twenty-five years old, a school-teacher in her first year of teaching.

In a small town in the South, in her role of teacher, she was caught up in trouble of a social and political nature. Nor was the town in any way prepared to let her off or laugh her down. She might have been younger than she was and still they would have viewed her with that dark, angry suspicion; they would still have called her offensive and dan-

gerous. And she was a good teacher too! For the children of
the parents who hated her so, she did make learning an ex-
citing, shining thing. She could not expect to be forgiven for
that either.

She stirred, got up, opened the drawer of the dresser, took
out her manicuring scissors, reached for the paper, the
Madison *Observer,* and cut out a single-column, front-page
item. Then she sank down at the table that served her as a
desk and read it through again.

FOUL BALL FATAL
TO PEEGRAM FAN;
BIRD ALSO KILLED

(*Special to Madison* Observer)

Peegram, May 13 — Ray
Hibbard, 11, died at midnight
from injuries received about
6:30 P.M. yesterday when he
was struck on the head by a
ball during a game here between Peegram High and
Lewisville.

The young boy was sitting
on the sidelines watching the
game when a foul ball hit him.
He was apparently not badly
hurt but became ill about 8
o'clock and was carried to the
hospital where he soon died.

Funeral will be held Satur-

day at 10 A.M. at the First
Baptist Church. He is survived
by his mother, Mrs. Carrie Er-
win Hibbard, and one brother,
Frederick. His father, Harry
Hibbard, while fishing last
summer, was drowned in the
Big Peegee River.

The young boy was hit during the last half of the ninth
inning when Lewisville was
at bat.

In the sixth inning, a sparrow flying across the diamond
between the pitcher and bat-
ter was hit by a pitched ball
and killed instantly.

A line of poetry, she could not remember what from,
offered itself to her mind—*He that spoke but now is no
longer in the room*. She pushed the clipping from her. *The
last half of the ninth*. She would not have to worry any
more about being unable to promote Ray Hibbard to the
sixth grade.

The direction had been so clear, this first year of her
first teaching job already drawing to its close under the
blackest cloud, when along came something like this, in the
shape of a *baseball*, and set such a curiously freakish seal
on the whole engagement as to make her want to . . . to
turn in her entrance ticket. Oh, said in the spirit of the game.

The last half of the ninth.

What had the bird to do with it? The bird could have been flying an inch higher or an inch lower—it need not have put in its two cents' worth.

She could not help it, she got up and made the restless tour of her rented room again. She was not prepared to say how many times, these past weeks, she had made this same tour. Peegram was such a small town as to be virtually without apartments, and young teachers engaged rooms in the houses of respectable citizens whose interest in their roomers' doings never waned, it would seem. Right now, somewhere in the lower regions, her movements were remarked. "She's walking around again, Josiah." (Her landlord's name was Josiah.) She shook a cigarette out of a pack she found on the dresser and brought her teeth down on it, as if intending to bite it in two, then forgot to light it, confronting the clipping from across the room. She would give half her next and last pay check for a pint of bourbon. But there, couldn't she be calm? She had not lost her bearings when that good citizen of Peegram (who? none knew) threw a rock through her window, wrapped around by a dime-store piece of paper with its penciled message, so heavily and inaccurately illiterate: GIT OUT OF TOWN WHILE THE GITTIN' IS GOOD. Her window shades were now more tightly drawn down, that was all. What time was it? Eight o'clock? She looked at her watch. It was eight o'clock exactly, on this night of May the thirteenth, Anno Domini 1955.

The tour of the room could not go on and on. The mirror she passed and repassed could not talk or warn her of the central paradox about herself: that she supposed she was an intellectual whereas it was "sex" that came flashing on in other people's minds the moment they set eyes on her. Offensive, dangerous: here was the reason. Yet the mirror was no help. She could never grasp it for very long at a time, and certainly not now, not even admitting that grasping it before it was too late might have a thing or two to do with her future welfare. She had met their looks with an innocence that was likely the worst sort of guilt. And she could have passed the mirror twenty times over and all it would have said to her now was, Teacher. Without the paradox, there was sufficient mockery.

She sat down on the bed and closed her eyes. Immediately, in the small convex theater of darkness behind her eyelids, Ray Hibbard appeared. He appeared in a faint cloud of chalk dust, trailing the eraser from his hand, saying "Yes ma'm," though not erasing the blackboard all the same; giving it the one feeble downward swipe. Saying, "Can I go now, Miss L?" She saying, "Yes, dear." That was yesterday, the moment in time when he, the dreamer, had climbed his dream to its summit, and when she, sensing this, sensed also that she must reach him then or never. But she was helpless, hedged in by her own ignorance and warned by the voice inside her which said she was indeed not his mother. And so he had dropped the eraser in the trough and left, still in his dream, and walked, dreaming, to the ball park, and the ball, hitting him, put him to sleep forever.

. . . If somebody should some day ask her what *really* had happened when she was teaching in Peegram, she should, if she were honest, reply, "I didn't get through to a child I loved." This somebody would then say, "Oh! That's not what we heard. We heard the whole town was thrown into an uproar on your account. We heard you were a Communist, or was it a nigger-lover, or maybe an atheist,

or all three, or anyway *something* setting morals at sixes
and sevens." She would say, "All that was nothing." She
hesitated. If honesty was her aim, she ought to add, "One
thing more. One other thing did happen in Peegram. I fell
in love—hopelessly, desperately, how I fought it; and it was
a point of pride with me that he should never find it out—
with *the preacher.*" But she asked permission of herself not
to dwell on this. No, not tonight. And not when the child
who was dead was the spiritual son and blood cousin of the
man she was in love with. And not when the entire structure
of love was erected on the one chance meeting of "that day."
How she had built it up—"that day"—the day in late October,
over five months ago, when what had happened was that she
had collided with him in the public library and, to steady
her, he had caught her quickly by the elbows and as quickly
let her go. He had caught her in order to steady her, to
prevent her from falling, which, as a reason, was reason
enough, except that it was not so. It was not why his hands
had found her elbows so unerringly or why he had smiled
that smile: she knew he was in love with her too, if hopelessly too, and even though he had proceeded on his way
with such calm. This preacher, Seth Erwin, was maybe forty
years old and was married to a pale, perfect lady. Martha
had the son of this union, as well as Ray, in her grade.

Ray. She opened her eyes and took the now limp and
offending cigarette from her mouth. She threw it toward
the wastebasket in a defiant and passionate gesture. She
wanted to know about the bird; about its relatives.

The clipping drew her. She had to gravitate toward it,
had to read it one more time, moving her lips over each
word, as she had used to do when she was a little girl, learn-

ing to read wrong. *His father, Harry Hibbard, while fishing last summer, was drowned in the Big Peegee River. . . .* She spied her roll book, a Riggs roll book, with its broken cover. She opened it, and opened her pen, and drew a wavering line through Ray Hibbard's name and all the zeros he had made.

Afterward—after the noise the pen made traveling across the double page—the silence was terrible. If it was not to be filled with thoughts, it was not to be filled with anything else. No tears came. But . . . a light May breeze lapped at the window shades.

2

She had traveled all over the world to come to Peegram. It was the gift her family (her mother was dead) gave her when she had completed her M.A. degree. They gave her the Grand Tour. So from London, from Paris, from Rome and Florence and Venice, from Heidelberg and Salzburg, Martha came to Peegram. Putting it to herself like that was no part of wisdom—she shivered rather than smiled. Did it have to be Peegram? she wondered, as if in the act of spreading out a map and ranging over all the little black dots with wide, still unreconciled eyes. Why not Lower Creek or Madison or even Gate City where she was born, one hundred and sixty-seven lovely miles away from Peegram? What had Peegram to recommend it—its courthouse with its hip roof and its square tower and its greenish Confederate hero on a horse? Its museum called Erwin House, in front of which were hitching posts instead of parking meters?

Oh, Peegram was too typical to be typical. A wandering
Peegramite, if asked where he hailed from, would invariably say Peegram first, then give the name of the state, one
of the original thirteen of course, as a negligent afterthought.
If Martha quite properly contended that she was a native
of the state, in Peegram there would be no comment. Her
father had emigrated from Austria when he was a boy, her
mother was from Kansas: no comment. George Washington
had stopped off in Peegram and one could not find out
whether he had slept here or not for the reason that there
was no comment.

And for all its self-contained smugness and snobbery,
Peegram was not broken down or moldering. That was the
secret, and it seemed like too much—Peegram should have
paid! But no, it was not the outsider's cliché concept of
"what is wrong with the South," simply quaint and lazy and
polite and utterly dissolute. Oh, no. Peegram had plagiarized
its past most stanchly and maintained itself in the present—
a present which had its nice slick patina of prosperity. Peegram was anything but asleep on its feet and had most
successfully grafted the twentieth-century answer to its an-
cestral tree. Peegram was dynamic. Its ossification and its
symptoms of inversion and self-congratulation—its inertia—
represented a terrific expenditure of energy and had their
own momentum, as Martha had had very good reason to find
out. And while people out in the state might think of Peegram as Mimosa Town (there was a festival every summer
around which the Chamber of Commerce made up its calendar even to naming its Man of the Year—there were many
many mimosa trees around), or speak feelingly of the beautiful river that held Peegram in the curve of an arm, or men-

tion with pleasure the blue haze that always seemed to be half hiding the mountains to the west, they tended to forget that Peegram was also the home of Royall Furniture, that same Royall Furniture of national reputation and fame; a tremendous wood-furniture concern. Not that the factories themselves were located in Peegram proper—they would have polluted the atmosphere; they were down the highway a piece, in an unincorporated clump simply called Royall, but they were Peegram's own, Peegram's lifeblood, and without any damfool unions calling the tune, sir. Peegram was a bird sanctuary.

Peegram was a baseball and church town, marvelously sustained and balanced.

Peegram was a Baptist town. Its old families and its prominent citizens were mostly Baptists. At first, this had seemed to Martha to be very odd, but she had learned since. She had learned that there are Baptists and Baptists. There are Freewill Baptists and Primitive Baptists and Wash Foot Baptists and Duck River Baptists and General Six Principle Baptists and Two-Seed-in-the-Spirit Predestination Baptists and also (because Baptist churches are politically and spiritually autonomous and complete in themselves) the Rich-and-Eminently-Respectable Baptists, and in Peegram the First Baptist Church was high church, definitely.

In Peegram there was a ruling family. The Erwin family, whose name the county proudly bore. The throne was shared by two—Carrie Erwin Hibbard, Ray's mother—Ray dead, Ray hit by a baseball; was she to believe it?—and Seth Erwin, pastor of the First Baptist Church. Seth Erwin, the preacher. Tracing with her finger the initials S. E. on the counterpane, concentrating, eyelids cast down, lips parting slightly. S. E.

There were Erwins around in plenty. The town was brimful
of them, so it seemed to Martha, Erwins and Ervins and
Irwins, but they were not *the* Erwins, which was of course
important. They were the mongrels, many of them indeed
colored. The thoroughbred Erwins went *clear* back, Seth
the son of Zebulon the son of Seth the son of Zebulon the son
of Seth the son of Zebulon the son of Seth the Pioneer, a
younger son of a minor squire coming from somewhere (Ire-
land, Martha believed) in the year 1740. . . . It was one
of these Erwins who had founded Royall Furniture, so
Martha had heard, and there were some rather mysterious
rumors to the effect that *one* Erwin had a hand in yet,
though why there should be any mystery involved Martha
could not imagine, unless it was a sort of joke the town liked
to think was being played on the Yankees who had presum-
ably taken Royall over.

In Peegram, conformity was the law. There was only the
one standard: it is, or it isn't, done. Anything—anybody—
accounted different, unless that "different" meant more of
the same and an outaveraging of the average, was automatically construed as a threat. So that the greatest loss
from frontier days might be reckoned that intense individ-
ualism they had fought and died so bravely in order to pre-
serve. As if that was the sacrifice they had been called upon
to make in return for identity in a machine age which does
seem to bring with it moral and mental assembly lines. Inasmuch as Fords are *almost* Cadillacs, was it so strange?

Martha, setting up as the intellectual and liberal, nevertheless knew, at the age of twenty-five, that there was one
thing she did not intend to be—a stranger—which was maybe
mostly why she had found herself in Peegram, such a little

bit of a town, on her first teaching job, to try to make a place for herself. How sad it was. Not Rome or Paris (they had issued the invitation) but Peegram had branded "S" upon her breast. "Stranger"—Peegram held the hot iron.

She traced the initials S. E. on the counterpane. . . . So she had had both Ray and Seth Erwin's son, William Morrison Erwin, in her grade. She had got too fond of both of them. This would have happened had she never laid eyes on Seth Erwin. And she had failed to see them as princes of the blood. They were just two little boys; one of them, Ray, dreamy and sensitive and delicate and with an overturned intelligence (challenging all her resources); the other pugnacious and stubborn, with a tidy mind and, yes, a rather alarming ability to love.

Everybody knew that Seth Erwin, as chairman of the school board, and Ray's mother, Carrie (and everybody called her Carrie, though it would have been a terrible faux pas for Martha to have done so), as Peegram's first lady or reigning queen, were nine parts responsible for the board's decision not to renew Martha's contract for teaching in Peegram next year. (Had Martha failed to promote Ray, which she would have had to do, they would have said it was her mean small way of getting even.) But this—the board's decision—civilized and quiet—was hardly worth its weight in the general tide of hate that had come moving in on her; nothing in the tide of everything else that began to happen and might be worsening as of this moment, she thought, raising her eyes to the window shade being so lightly tapped by the breeze; waiting for the next development, simply because there was nothing else to do but wait.

It was better for her, in her mind, so restless and active

as to refuse the passive role of waiting, if she went back.
Not to that time when Roger Patton, the principal, had
called her down for failing to begin each school day with
"I pledge allegiance to the Flag" and the Lord's Prayer,
telling her it amounted to law. She had asked her questions
—Did they want patriotism to be official and automatic? Was
it that they were free to be Christians?—but she had given in.
And not to the time, not so long afterward, when he told
her *it had come to his attention* that she did not belong to
a church or go to church—explaining so painstakingly to
her that in a small town one simply had to go and that it
didn't have anything to do with beliefs, not any more, and
she must quick join a church if she wanted to stay on, that
otherwise it didn't matter how good she was in her job,
saying it was a part of the general contract with society now,
like wearing clothes or driving on the right-hand side of the
road. Oh, she should have resigned then and there, or else
done what he said she must instead of assuring him he did
not have the right to bring the matter up. But could she
have told Roger Patton that she *couldn't* go to church,
because she could not have endured hearing Seth Erwin
preach a sermon on Love? He might have told her there
were other churches. She had had to make the battle personal, had had to hold out, since she could not escape thinking it was Seth Erwin who had really challenged her, slipping the challenge to poor Roger Patton to hand on to her,
and it was perfectly clear that she had to hate either Seth
Erwin or herself.

She considered that she was religious, but she did not find
God in church and she did not believe that many preachers
did, especially these handsome ones who must have had a

big question to settle, whether to enter the ministry or the
movies. She could sooner see herself in love with a racketeer
than a preacher! As for the town, if the town guessed that
she who spelled "sex" to every man should dare, even in her
dreams, to set her cap for their Man of God, what would
they do to her, they who had cast the first stone? Oh, wicked.
Never mind, they must never, never find out. Her own finding out, her own admission that it was love and not hate she
felt for the preacher, was very recent, coming in the wake of
painful recent events. For weeks, months, refusing to con-
cede that she had crumbled at one touch, one smile; or that,
to her, her own elbows had become sacred. It was only with
this admission that she had put the interpretation (that he
loved her too) on the smile smiled so long ago. Granting Seth
Erwin a brain and sensitiveness making it worse; his reminding her from the first of Ray, or Ray of him; his having undoubtedly once had a soul to tamper with. Unhappy woman
that she was, going to church meaning giving in to *him*. She
could not seem to help holding it against him that he was
tall and slender, had close fair hair and strange green eyes.
All right. But the point was, she was religious. And he and
his brand of religion! She had heard about those prayer
rooms out at Royall Furniture, installed shortly before a
union tried to hold an election there. Seth Erwin's inspired
idea, everybody agreed. And it was also on his recommendation that Royall hired a full-time pastor-counselor and hung
up religious mottoes all over the walls under the pin-up girls.
The mottoes were in plain view: *'Tis better to give than to
receive; Lay not up for yourselves treasures on earth.* The
number of shares of Royall common stock Seth Erwin
owned, that would be the only hidden factor. . . . Ah, her

mind was all over the place, but she did not propose to go
back over all those weeks of inner turmoil, when it was as if
she were sleepwalking and unable to wake herself. She most
certainly did not need to review the final warning Roger
Patton had issued her—to be as silent as the tomb—and as if
she had no notion that the initial Supreme Court decision
on segregation in the schools had been hanging over the
nation and the state and Peegram for almost a year, or that
the Court's promised review of this decision was also hanging over them. Experts (even in the national magazines)
claiming it was *this* state where a new attitude toward the
Negro had been born, where the Negro was well off, when
the truth was it was in this state that "separate but equal"
had been carried maybe the farthest, with its program of
bigger and better schools (although most of them were
still shameful) and equal pay for Negro teachers and so on
and so on—the Negro bribed "to keep his place" and the
white man's conscience oozing virtue. By its own word this
being the state that had set out to prove, and had proved,
that "separate but equal" could not only work but work
beautifully. Martha did not need Roger Patton to tell her
that those experts who thought this state would be one of the
ones to submit without a struggle to desegregation in its
schools thought woefully wrong. Its sense of virtue was out-
raged. If the Court did not back down, the state could be
expected to resist in almost direct proportion to effort ex-
pended in the past decades. Already feeling was running
high, pressure groups were mushrooming. Any fool ought
to be able to see that the state was girding itself. But Roger
Patton's function was not to make all this clear to Martha,
it was to communicate his fear to her. (He could have

known, by osmosis, where she stood, what her position was.)
The desegregation issue, he told her, was a *school* issue, and
she was a *schoolteacher*, vulnerable *at best*—his eyes glancing quickly over and off her, when he said that, very effec-
tively letting her know that no matter what her views, she
was the wrong protagonist for this cause and could only
do it harm. Giving her to understand that it was her duty,
now, to grasp the meaning of her beauty for longer than five
minutes; that she could no longer traffic with that innocence
which amounted to guilt; that circumstances required that
she see herself only as others saw her. She was frightened.
Frightened: sitting mum the times her landlord Josiah Sparks
held forth; in the Teachers' Room, sitting quiet on the oc-
casions when her colleagues damned the NAACP and all
nigger-lovers, or described in graphic language what they
would do the day the school they taught in let a nigger past
its doors. Roger Patton said that in Peegram the desegregation issue wasn't dynamite but Pandora's box. She understood.

Peegram's Negro population was only about twelve per
cent, but the ones Martha had seen around seemed servile
and slovenly, pompous and fawning, very much the descend-
ants of slaves, and characteristically flaunting the outlandish
combinations of castoff clothes of the white folks they worked
for. As if, undercurrent, and in keeping with the will for
survival, was a general submission to stereotype: flattened
face, the eternal pout of thick lips, the impertinent mournful-
ness of a languid and enormous stare. Except in the capacity
of janitors or maids, Negroes did not work at Royall, of
course. (The state, with a few trifling exceptions, had barred
the Negro from industry when it was evident that industry

would have to save the day.) Martha gathered that the superior and energetic among them made a policy of clearing out.

Peegram was too typical to be typical. Peegram was a storm center. Martha sensed this, except as she would have supposed the Negroes too intimidated and dependent to make any sort of stand for themselves; themselves terrified of any move toward desegregation and more violently opposed to it than the white people whose houses they kept in order. One could not imagine their introducing test cases in the courts. One could imagine the one lone rebel who might try, not as being lynched, but as losing his job and, if he persisted, finding his old jalopy wrecked or his home in ashes, the work of his colored neighbors, one would hear afterward, with the uneasy suspicion that it was true. Peegram and Erwin County, of which it was the county seat, ought to be, then, instead of a storm center, a protected cove where "voluntary segregation" could be expected to work without a ripple? Sometimes Martha had thought yes, more often no, even before Roger Patton had issued his warning. Feeling was so savage! As if Peegram were spoiling for a fight or two, to make its position irrevocably clear. One noticed, in the stores, the rash of Confederate flags and caps as toys for children. On every hand one heard again allusions to "the damn Yankee." World War I and World War II; Civil War I and Civil War II? God, what are we doing? The wrong night for speculation. And no more floundering. It wasn't even those weeks of her own frightened silence calling her coward that concerned her now. It was what had brought those weeks to their abrupt culmination, with every

seemingly isolated circumstance since her coming to Peegram
turning out to be intimately related and only waiting for
the correct moment to click into position with military pre-
cision. One, two, three, and the trap was sprung.

3

The trap was sprung in her own room at school, in April,
in calendar time less than a month ago. It was during Current Events. And a question was specially "current." Would
the Court—*could* the Court possibly be expected to reverse
its decision, or at least provide some comfortable loopholes?
The children would have heard a lot of talk. Indeed, in those
dangerously deceptive two-dimensional aspects of television,
what they hadn't heard and seen didn't amount to much.
Appropriately enough, it was Seth Erwin's son, William
Morrison Erwin, who brought it up.

"Miss L," he had said. "About this here Supreme Court
decision."

"Yes," she said, fainting away inside. She allowed them a
great deal of freedom of discussion in the Current Events
period. They had discussed schizophrenia, the crime rate,
nuclear fission and fusion, whammies, Dwight Eisenhower,
jet planes, NATO and the Lord knew what all else. Could
she let them down now? Shut the door? Sit on the lid of the
box, though it was Pandora's? No. But there was no doubt
about it, William Morrison's statement certainly blew the
lid off! The room was in a near uproar. The children were
all suddenly talking at once, cutting in on each other, cutting

each other off; introducing, as she had never heard them do
before, their parents' pronouncements and opinions as the
final word. "My dad says" and "my mother says." Their
faces flushed and hectic. Unable to sit even remotely still;
beside themselves. Such violence in agreement—because
they all certainly seemed to be in complete agreement—she
had never witnessed.

"My dad says we'll close all the schools first!"

"My mama said she'd sooner see me dead than in the same
school with one nigger."

"My pop says it's *our* tax dollars and if they don't like what
they get, let 'em go back to Africa where they come from."

"Yeah."

"And we fought one war, my dad says, and we might just
have to fight it over. And he says . . ."

"And he says . . ."

"And she says . . ."

"Over his dead body . . ."

"Blood is gonna flow, that's what."

But William Morrison, frowning steadily, wanted to get
the legal side straight. He said, "Why *is* it unconstitutional,
Miss L, when they already got their schools? What's it about?
If it's 'separate but equal,' what's wrong with that? I don't
get it."

So Martha began to speak, slowly and quietly. "Our
country was founded . . . 'equal' as meaning not equal in
the length of our feet or the size of our brains, but equal in
opportunity and treatment under a government of law. . . .
Our forefathers . . ."

(She looked at her children. History in one easy lesson,
she thought in her despair.)

". . . equality and freedom, put to the test . . . brothers fighting each other . . . a young nation that would have stopped being a nation if the South had won . . . the years of Reconstruction . . . the empty fields and the burned-down houses, the carpetbaggers and all the broken promises."

(All the Confederate flags and Confederate caps in the dime stores.)

"When a law—or war—sets a people free, that's nothing until it happens inside us . . . as if there were a second battlefield inside us no Northerner could reach.

"Maybe," she said, "it's *our* turn to set the Negroes free. *Maybe* we have come far enough to consider the Supreme Court decision 'ours' instead of 'theirs.' Maybe we can finally be Americans first and Southerners second. Anyhow, I think the Supreme Court believes so."

(Martha, Martha.)

She said, "The Supreme Court has held that no person can be turned away from a public school because of his color. We're all Americans together. If there's a heaven, I don't think there'll be two gates, one marked White and the other Colored. I don't believe Saint Peter is going to say, 'Colored souls please seat from the rear.'"

(No one laughed.)

She reviewed the small, shocked faces, tomorrow's grown-up faces, before she said, "I'd be happy to see some Negro children in here with us. And I hope I wouldn't 'see' them too much, one way or the other, after the first few days. I hope we'd get along just about the way we do now. And it would be more real. Do you see?"

Silence, the kind louder than thunder. William Morrison,

with that stubborn, tidy mind of his, was the one who broke it. He said, "You mean, Miss L, you're *for* de-seggerga-tion? Intergation?"

And she, of course, must sign her death warrant formally, dot the *i*'s and cross the *t*'s. "Yes, I am," she said. "Although I hope it can move ahead pretty slowly and begin in cities and counties where it could be expected to work best, where bad feeling is least strong."

The silence returned. This was her first experience of a class frozen solid against her, of massed ten-and-eleven-year-old outrage and shock. She would not have dreamed it was possible (she was fiddling with a ruler on her desk) that there *was* any one single common spring she could have touched and produced this. Who would have believed that in one short decade on this earth prejudice could have set so hard? She had lost them, and why? How? Because she had dared to try "to educate"? Didn't it give you pause, when it was children who would be directly affected by the Court's decision and any program of integration? And when this was a future which it was up to "the little ones" really to decide and while they were little too, how nevertheless her bringing the issue in here seemed a crime? But, she reminded herself, she hadn't brought it; they had. Looking at her watch, she saw that the 3:20 bell was about to ring. She felt very tired. Even the timing was wrong. They would go home now and carry their astonishing news, still warm, still hot from the oven, to their parents. She turned away from them and began idly flipping over the maps on the map stand. Then she heard William Morrison speaking again—*sotto voce*, but not much; only technically was it a stage whisper. She heard him say, "We better not go telling this around, see? Folks'll get sore. Our folks will. They'll say she's a nigger-lover and *we* know Miss L's O.K. Anybody goes out of here telling on her, I'll bust 'em one, see, on the nose."

"Yeah," she heard Tad say in the same loud whisper, Tad and William Morrison being the leaders. "Me too."

She felt her eyes mist over, she saw her outstretched hand waver and fall. And although she knew it would be too much for them, knew they would "tell" now, if only to take her side (William Morrison himself would be the first); although it wasn't even what she would want, she felt alive again and warm. She turned back around and faced them.

"It's not a secret," she said with a smile, with the sense of being able to make up for all the weeks of frightened silence. "What I think and believe isn't a secret."

But William Morrison glared comprehensively around, retracting nothing; Tad did the same.

Quite suddenly Ray, who had seemed half asleep, who was typically and always half asleep, and the only child in the room who had held aloof throughout . . . Quite suddenly, Ray was talking. His words came crowding each other, while his thin, high-pitched voice struggled, carrying them. "Dogs don't care," he said. "Dogs don't even know *which* is white and *which* is black and *which* is spotted. Dogs don't stick up their nose at another dog 'cause he's a different *color*. So if they don't care, I don't care. Black is good as white. Dogs got more sense than *most* folks."

Then it happened, what they all always dreaded, but this time with such special reference: tears began sliding down Ray's cheeks without his being aware of it. He would cry like that, without knowing he was crying. It seemed to

Martha that invariably, when this happened, there was some
buried connection between whatever he was saying or doing
and his father, whose name, as far as Martha knew, had
never crossed his lips once since (as she would imagine) the
day of his father's drowning. (It was to cross his lips before
he went to the ball park, but that time was not yet.) He had
stood up to speak his piece about people and dogs and now
he stood there with his hands clenched, crying, and everybody, including Martha, felt saved by the bell, by the welcome routine of collecting books and gear and filing out.
She dared not stop Ray.

She didn't know if they would fight him or not when they
got outside. In the first place, there were those tears to be
dealt with. But also, it might be one thing, allowing their
teacher her views, and even perhaps defending her for them.
It might be altogether another to find one among themselves
—who was for integration because dogs were. She recalled
something she had heard about the boy's father's favorite
fishing companion having been a Negro. Maybe there was
some connection there, because she felt, however obscure it
was, that Ray had gone to bat, not for her but for his father
beneath whose canceled-out image he was crumbling.

She got to the window in time to see William Morrison
hitting Ray, with several of the others gathered around.
They were on the sidewalk, on the far side of the street from
the school. One look was enough to decide what sort of
fight it was, a token one on William Morrison's part, but
with puny little Ray fighting back for all he was worth. Not,
then, because of what Ray had said, but because of his tears.
It was the only way the children knew of handling them—
to give him something to cry *about*, though not too much.

Somebody began shouting at them from the schoolyard and
they were breaking up, with William Morrison pulling Ray
along by one arm, and Ray hitting out blindly at him. It was
in the classroom that Ray was typically half asleep. Out-
doors, on the playground, at games and sports and tests of
strength, at which he was doomed to fail, he came heart-
breakingly alive. Martha could almost hear William Mor
rison calling Ray "screw." "Cut it out, you screw." "Screw"
was William Morrison's word; he used it as a noun, as a
contraction of "screwball," Martha guessed. William Morrison was as close to her heart as Ray was, maybe closer, and
not because he was his father's son, but because he was
totally himself. He bossed her along with everybody else;
it was his indisputable role in life. He was the one most
responsible for turning a "notoriously tough" class into a
good one. Apparently there was something about her that
demanded his endorsement and protection; also, he was
just tough enough himself to direct miracles. (He always
made her feel one hundred per cent woman.) William
Morrison and Ray. And between them, hadn't they fixed
her? The one: "About this here Supreme Court decision
. . ." The other: "Dogs don't care . . ." Between them, Seth
Erwin's son and Carrie Hibbard's son, these princes of the
blood, had done her in completely. She had to smile.

She went upstairs to Roger Patton's office. It was better
it came from her first. . . . Her children were rocked to
their foundations. And for the first time (all these "first
times") she had set them against their parents and their
rearing; or rather, she had openly opposed what she had
known were their parents' views, making it necessary for
the children to choose, something she did not believe in

doing and had before this so carefully avoided. Well, that was done too; was what she had done to them (doing them in?) for better, for worse? The new words right this minute at work in their hearts and heads.

She had to wait awhile in Roger's outer office. When had they started in calling each other "Roger" and "Martha"? In the midst of one of their altercations, no doubt. It was one of those things, that Roger liked Martha from the first, and she him, each recognizing the teacher in the other, she supposed. . . . But Roger didn't really need to have—and such copies!—Gainsborough's "Blue Boy" on one wall and Whistler's "Mother" returning the compliment from the other, did he? Did he have to make up his mind to every cliché there was? What life-purpose. It might be rather fun to slip in here some evening and substitute Picasso's "Blue Boy" for the Gainsborough and perhaps Cézanne's wonderful "Woman with a Coffee Pot" for the Whistler. Roger would be the last to notice them of course, but when at last somebody pointed them out to him, she could imagine him staring from one to the other drunkenly, lost in depths of admiration, before ordering them down.

Poor, funny Roger. She wondered if the man stepping up to the scaffold ever thought, "Poor, funny hangman." Roger was born tired and diffusely anxious, anxious in his muscles and the walls of his blood vessels, and more perceptive than was good for him. He was prematurely bald, with the inevitable nickname among the children of Egg Head, and his ears stuck straight out from his head, reminding Martha of a car with its doors open. His clothes were ill-fitting and always wrinkled. His body was a longer, more disarranged oval than his head. Altogether his appearance led you to believe you were dealing with a hick. Added to this was his habit of keeping his attention riveted to some small current disaster, such as the plumbing in the boys' rest room or the radiator in 202 which refused to come on. That way, his grasp of bigger things, which was unmistakably fine, was held at bay. Roger was so determined to be mediocre! Martha felt very sorry for him today. She wished she could help by complaining first about that window in her room which stuck. But when he was ready to see her, she found she had to tell him without preamble what had happened. When she was through, he dropped his head to his desk and covered its shining baldness with both hands.

"Oh, my God," he moaned. "Have you come to offer your resignation?" he then asked, lifting his head higher than he had need to.

She could not help it, and it was most inopportune, but she laughed. "No," she said. "You'll really have to kick me out now, Roger. I just wanted you to hear it—and the straight of it—from me, first."

"Yes—*first*," he said, looking balefully from her to the telephone. "It's a wonder it isn't ringing already. This is the end!"

"All right, Roger. But I want you to realize it came up in the most natural way—I hadn't opened my mouth to anybody else—I took warning from you. I can't help wondering what you would have had me do. (What would you have done?) Go against my own beliefs? Deny them? Shut the kids up? I've quite a lot of tact, you know, Roger."

Seeing his look of astonishment, she had to laugh again. "I do have tact," she said. "And I'm no trouble maker. (I don't expect people *not* to go to church because I don't.)

The only thing in the world wrong with me is that I happen
to take a few beliefs seriously."

Roger's look when she said that—"the only thing in the
world wrong with me . . ."—caused her to look away. "*You!*"
his look had cried.

"Good," he said in a low, tight voice. "I hope you stand
ready to give up your job for their sake."

Getting angry again: "One question, Roger. Is this a de-
mocracy or not?"

"You wave a red flag—two red flags, one after the other—
at the bulls and then want to get philosophical," he said
bitterly. "You won't go to church and now this, the one and
only other spot you could hit at and know for certain they'd
react by howling for your blood. And I did warn you, it's
not as if I didn't! Genius. You're fired—as good as fired."
(He was getting up.) "Good luck."

"Thank you, Roger." But regarding him with wonder.
All this feeling! She had the odd notion that he might have
been putting up some sort of fight for her; spreading the
word, maybe, that she was a Catholic or a Unitarian or the
member of some other faith not represented in Peegram,
which, while bad enough, might just serve to keep her here.
She would not put it beyond him. How angry he was. She
said, more gently, "I hope this means you'll give me a good
letter of recommendation. I may need one."

"What it means," he said, "is that I shall feel obligated
to speak the truth. That's no less than you should ask. And
that includes a statement of your stand on segregation. And
that means, my dear Martha, you might as well move on to
another part of the country. No school in this state is going to
touch you. I'm glad you have your Master's."

Leaving the office, she was brooding over it: was Roger right? Surely not. Surely there would be a place for her in some city school. In Gate City, if nowhere else. "You don't miss it till the well runs dry." She wouldn't miss the state unless she had to leave it. Most of the time, she thought it was a sorry, no-good state, populated by drones and idiots. Yet when she was most busy running it down, she was apt to be most busy loving it. It was a state that rather wormed its way inside you, its hills and its woods and all. . . . If belonging was her goal, and it wasn't simply Peegram that wouldn't have her . . . But the Legislature, right now in heated session, the Board of Commissioners, the Governor's known sentiments . . . Ah, Roger *could* be right—he was always right, with Whistler instead of Cézanne. Her feet were walking down the hall, but the rest of her was standing stock still. What had she done?

4

"To teach is to love." She had read that somewhere, probably in the *Reader's Digest.*

She knew what she had done; oh, she knew. Was it for not knowing that she had maintained her frightened silence for so long? Yet she had not the slightest conception of the enormity of it! Perhaps no one else did, not even Roger Patton. Perhaps it was one of those incidents that trigger history, because all is in readiness, at this time and in this place. How many telephone calls had there been that same night?—with Josiah's wife standing by, tight lipped, and smelling of wet feathers. How many mothers had placed

their outrage on record? "Now I just didn't know whether
to believe my Sue Anne. Is it true, Miss Lyerly, etc.?" "Yes,
it is true, etc." The modest beginning. Could anybody have
guessed how it would pile up: how Ray's words about folks
and dogs would sound, third-hand; how they would pass
like fire in a dry month over a dry field; how they would
be taken as the chiefest "rational" argument against "the
godless one," this unspeakable perversion of *Carrie's* son.
Or how the town, as one being, could rise up and know, as
one being, exactly where it stood. To Martha, this was the
most amazing thing of all, the town being solid. Or how,
finally, she caused them to run amok, in the nonrational
sphere, what with "sex" flashing on in their minds not just
when they saw her but every time they spoke her name or
thought about her. She drove them wild; and herself both
aware and unaware of this. The color of her hair and eyes
was all wrong and the almost olive cast of her skin was
against her too. (Her mother was from *Kansas,* was it?)

The very next morning, in her free period, she ran into
Roger in the hall.

"Calls," he said, glaring at her.

She said, "Yes." (Meekly.)

He was pale—gray-looking. Obviously, he had not slept.

"Well, let them instigate it, then," he said belligerently.
"I'm not going to. They know what they can do. Let them
bring it up through channels. I'll tell Miles Lathrop that.
(Miles Lathrop was the superintendent.) I'll wait for them.
You might as well know that, see?"

Poor Roger, she thought. Had he found himself, against
his will and better judgment, taking up for her again? But
there was no time—not even a minute, not even a second—to

wait. They turned (in one accord) and saw the massive figure of Carrie Hibbard filling the door. Behind her was Seth Erwin. They—Roger and Martha—shot each other one swift, deep look. "This is it," Roger muttered. And—she would not forget it, Carrie and Seth Erwin could not possibly have failed to see it—he put out his hand and pressed hers.

"Don't you do it, Roger," she breathed. "Don't you even try to buck them."

"I can't," he said simply.

Then she felt herself blushing up, her resentment pricking like needles in the presence of Seth Erwin, standing there, cool, poised, freshly arrived to chop her head off, this man she loved. Yes, she had to pick this particular moment to know it beyond any more doubting or torturing of herself; it was this particular moment she had chosen to realize she had crumbled that October day, five months ago. Lighting all her secret places in the dimness of the hall. Subtle and beautiful, if damned. *The preacher!* My God, she thought, it's all I need at this stage—to be in love with *him*. No grown-up edition of William Morrison, but—and how it seemed to haunt her!—the grown-up and ruined edition of Ray. Odd thing to think, with Carrie, Ray's mother, standing right beside him. The only man she had ever seen who made her want to give up her own identity. My God, she thought, it is terrible, terrible, to be a woman.

They did not speak. What had they to say to each other? Roger hurried them off, clucking in his throat and glancing back at her with his pale, martyred face that went on and on because he was bald. . . .

So they fired her, quickly and quietly and decently, informing her only that her contract would not be renewed for the following year. Hoping thereby to avoid trouble. (If they could have spirited her away at once!) They spread the word of their action, like balm, on the angry and festering town. Very civilized. But it did not work.

One of the reasons it did not work was on account of the children themselves. The children decided on a course of their own upon discovering themselves, for the first time in their lives, in the sustained limelight of that remote adult world of their elders, where never before had what they said or did been taken seriously—it was, was it not, their words that had been taken and blown up to size? The children became impressed with their own sudden and peculiar importance. As if by some happenstance they had all been given stilts and found themselves walking around taller than their fathers, if slightly more vulnerable to spills. Ray was one of them, Ray had leaped to fame, and their collective fame was only a little less than his. Over the days, were they not asked to repeat again and again their "evidence"?

Ordinarily they might not even have been made aware of their teacher's getting the ax. Certainly they would not have been made sensitive to what lay behind it. They would have supposed such doings, and such comings and goings of teachers, merest routine and no affair of theirs. And had they heard of it at all, they would have been vaguely sorry she was not to be around any longer, but *they* after all would be through with her before that distant time. As for the adults, knowing of the foolish loyalties of children, they would ordinarily have made it a point not to discuss a teacher's dismissal in their children's presence—in fact, all discussion would have stopped the moment a child came around. Now, all *was* topsy-turvy, the very sight of the children, these innocent small victims of witchcraft, these fruits of their own wombs, being exactly what set them off. Could they stand by and allow a dangerous philosophy to rub off on *these?* No, it was a sacred obligation—the children had to be made whole again, they had to be cleansed, examined again and again for symptoms of subversion. ("Are you really saying, Sue Anne, that she said she'd be *happy* to mix niggers up with *you?* Well, now, tell Daddy now, tell your daddy what you think of such talk as that.") Cleansing. If there had been brain washing, there had to be counter brain washing. And no one could help it if tempers were involved; if in the process there was one emotional explosion after another. So of course the children heard plenty. They heard that the last of May might not be soon enough to get that nigger-loving atheist woman out of here. Some of them heard their parents say they would just be damned if they were going to accept the grades *that woman* gave their offspring—they'd rather see their child repeat a grade than accept any verdict she might hand out—why, they would be for wiping the slate completely clean, for starting the fifth grade all over in the fall and as if this year had never been. Some of them heard their teacher called those names, with the dark hints about her past and the blood that ran in her veins, only thinly veiled. Some also heard her called slut and whore.

William Morrison Erwin knew who it was that had engineered the action of the board. (After that first fateful day, segregation was not mentioned in Martha's room; this was the children's decision—in their room, the issue was now taboo. They went ahead, doggedly, with arithmetic and spelling.) William Morrison, with that stubborn look on his

face getting stubborner by the day, organized what he called
the Junior Citizens' Committee. And that did it! That was
the last straw. That was heresy of the sort the town, for all
its fears, had certainly never dreamed of. That Carrie Hibbard's child, and now Seth Erwin's child (styling himself
chairman)—that all their children—because this committee
(the *Junior Citizens'* Committee, if you please!) was composed of the entire 5-A (probably under penalty of
bashed noses) and some few strays from other rooms and
grades, pulled in by its chairman—should take the part of
that woman! The committee intended visiting the school
board in a body, its loudly avowed purpose being to protest
their teacher's dismissal. What made it worse—if anything
could have made it worse—giving answer to answer, as you
might say, in a way to make a person blush—was that the
children had their "line," as dictated by William Morrison.
William Morrison said they must absolutely not let on that
they had turned into nigger-lovers like Ray, or anything
aproaching it, and that old Ray must swear to keep his
mouth positively shut about black dogs and white dogs and
all such as that. William Morrison said that what they
must do was to very politely explain to the board that they
had not minded book-learning under Miss L, something that
sure never had happened before, and then they would take
turns spieling off multiplication tables and pomes and stuff
like that, to prove their point. And *then* they would say,
very polite, that it was their idea Miss L ought to stick
around. And if *that* didn't work, William Morrison said,
they would get up a *pe*-tition which everybody would sign.

Martha got wind of this committee and took the liberty
of interrupting it when it was in session. ("William Morri-

son," she said, "you wait awhile. Some day you'll be governor.") She told the committee members she very much
appreciated their efforts on her behalf, but what was done
was now done, and she thought it would be better if, as a
committee, they dissolved. She told them it was her belief
that what was done was nobody's fault at all. And if they
wanted to do what would please her, why, they could all
study hard next year. She would try to write them postcards and let them know how she was getting on. She
could see that most of them were amenable, but William
Morrison was not. He said they had already made an appointment with the board and they were going to keep it.
He said his old man was chairman of *that* and *he* was chairman of this! Realizing the committee had gone as far as it
had in actually making an appointment, Martha had felt
sick. She had to be her most persuasive. She had finally to
say that if William Morrison really wanted to help her, he
must cancel that appointment himself. She did not like to
put it that way, but she could not allow them to get any
deeper into the business than they were. Whoever had heard
of a whole troop of fifth-graders descending on a school
board?

Afterward, after the committee was formally dissolved
and they had all repaired to Mr. Lambeth's drugstore for
ice cream (Martha supposed the town would put its own
interpretation on this too, on her paying out for forty-seven
cones, doubtless saying she had bribed the children to form
the committee in the first place and was now bribing them
to break it up, for being scared, for having failed to foresee
the grimness of consequences; and much more of this and
she would end up with a persecution complex; but wasn't

it clear that Mr. Lambeth, while distraught, poor man—the
present depreciation to his property being enough to drive
him right out of his mind—was missing nothing), after they
had all gone their various ways home, Martha returned to
her rented room and cried.

5

It was quite true, it didn't matter that the Junior Citizens'
Committee did not in fact go to the board. That it had ever
existed was intolerable. Its fame became as great as the
fame of Ray's words. A very garbled version of the ice cream
party was spread by Mr. Lambeth, and what he claimed to
have heard Martha telling the children was a revelation.
Business was extremely brisk at his emporium. "And then
she said, wasn't it too bad they hadn't thought to bring
some little chocolate friends in for some of this chocolate
cream." Two children from Martha's room were withdrawn,
one of them Sue Anne who was about the brightest in
there. Let the truant officer—there was no truant officer in
Peegram—let the school authorities dare to object! It was
said that stricken parents were forming committees themselves.

Martha no longer went to the Teachers' Room. Eating at
the school cafeteria became so painful she took to skipping
lunch. She did not realize she was avoiding going downtown
until she went. She had broken one of the glass knobs on
the dresser in her room and had made up her mind she
would replace it, if it was the last thing she did. So she
had gone downtown and into Peegram Hardware to see

what she could find. There was a clump of fairly rough-looking men just inside the door. One of these Roger Patton had once pointed out to her as "the notorious Andy Boyd," she recalled, but did not recall notorious for what, if indeed he had told her. She had passed them and, in passing, heard some one of them mutter "That's her"—and gone on her way to the back of the store. The store was dark and had that dark smell of grease and seeds and sacked grain and puppies and parakeets. She approached a counter laid out in squares of screws, nuts, bolts, hinges, surely door knobs, when she heard the men's voices swell up suddenly. No clerk came to help her, no clerk was about to come. She had best leave. She told herself it was absurd to be so alarmed, noting at the same instant that there wasn't a back door; she started. The men had the door blocked; she saw they didn't move, as she came on; that all their eyes were riveted on her; that, possibly, they did not intend to move. She said to herself, "Go on—you can't stop now—just keep walking." But she was unable to obey her own command. She did stop, and smile, and say softly, "Excuse me, please." They opened a small way, but making it necessary that she press against them, and she heard the obscenities they breathed down the cleft between her breasts. Outside, it was all she could do to keep from running, until she reached the square and turned the corner. Oh, she grasped it forever, the meaning of her beauty. "Stranger" and "scarlet letter" both, iron-hot in the cleft between her breasts. If she could ever again forget it for five minutes at a stretch, that was all.

She decided she would not go downtown again unless she had to—and found she did not have to, after that. There was a wretched little grocery store two blocks from where

she lived into which she crept when there was nothing else
for it.

Roger did not have to hint to her that it was better she
keep out of sight as much as possible, and out of mind. But
the rock, wrapped round with its message, came sailing
through her window all the same. And why Mrs. Josiah did
not throw her out—or at least abrogate her kitchen privileges
—was a mystery, unless Roger had brought some sort of
pressure to bear on her.

They called off a scheduled meeting of PTA. It was just
wiser, Roger said, for people not to get together in groups
right now. (Groups, crowds, mobs.)

Roger took to picking her up in his car. Like that. As if
it were (suddenly) on his way. He would be parked by the
curb when she came out in the mornings. Disgruntled,
elaborately sleepy. He would walk with her through the hall
at the school, as far as her room. He would take her home
too, telling her abruptly what time he would be down for
her.

It would take her a time to recover herself—those smallest
actions and inner thoughts, no longer her own—to get over
the hurt, the appalling stitches in her heart. And yet she
was not unmindful that the world was bigger than Peegram.
If she could discount the person with whom she was in
love, the manipulator and the cool observer, she did not
feel she had failed, not in the deepest sense. She managed
to write her sister some fairly amusing letters about it,
letters in which she turned poor Roger, with his bald head
and the wrinkled fury of his clothes, into a veritable Sancho
Panza, and for which she felt a mild sort of guilt. She would
hold out somehow till the last of May. She would not be

running the gauntlet of hate forever. Even the pangs of
desperate love would subside. That was her frame of mind
—the tension mounting, mounting—until the baseball hit
Ray.

6

One thing she had tried to do—and now it seemed important. Following her hunch—that Ray had made his speech
on folks and dogs in defense not of her but of his father—
she had asked Roger, really her only source of contact and
information since her disgrace, about Harry Hibbard. There
seemed to be a kind of mystery surrounding him, one she
could not put her finger on inasmuch as no one of the things
she did know about him seemed mysterious in the least. He
was drowned while fishing less than a year ago. He had been
a successful salesman representing Royall Furniture. He was
Carrie's husband. He was a one-time athlete, and this she
had known, oddly enough, before she ever came to Peegram, because his name was still spoken with reverence in
university football circles. Obviously he stood for something important in the town—the very stuff and substance
of "Peegram Hero," she would have vowed. She had taken
for granted that that was what Ray's struggle was about,
that he was trying to emulate the father-embodied Peegram
ideal of Peegram strengths and virtues, and as still further
complicated because so obviously repeated in his older,
vigorous, extroverted brother Fred whom Martha had seen
around, but which he—Ray—was constitutionally unable
to realize, and with all the resultant waste of talent and

energy. Helping to free him of such an obligation and such
a desire—that was her wish and what she had defined as her
own part in it. Herself setting a high value on sensitiveness
and imagination and intelligence of the nonprofit sort, qualities he had, but that Peegram people not only set no store in
(not even bothering with lip service where boys were
concerned) but considered exactly the constellation of
traits most upsetting to the general good and the one they
therefore pressed hardest to kill. But Ray had to find himself through those qualities if he was ever to find himself
at all. It was what had drawn her to him from the first.
He was like a little angel; you would almost not believe
in his beauty anywhere, not on earth and not in heaven.
But those tears that came on him so often? For all her
efforts she had not been able to reach him all year; the
children, hitting him, reached him better than she did. But
it was as if the damned state of her love for the man Ray so
reminded her of committed her to making every effort to
help save Ray if she could, and even though she could not
always see how it followed. Since he had spoken his piece,
she very definitely felt some crisis in Ray was shaping up.
Then her hunch teasing her toward action: supposing she
was not wrong—why, how possibly, could such a model
father need defending?

So she put it to Roger—rather casually and offhandedly—
one afternoon, when he had come down to her room to take
her home. She said something like "What sort of man was
Harry Hibbard, Roger?" An expression came over his face—
of anguish, perhaps, and a kind of concentrated exaspera-
tion. As if to say "I knew it!" or "Couldn't I have foretold
that you would ask *that*!" Whatever the look added up to,

it got more and more in-turned and he did not utter a
syllable.

"But what have I done?" she had said. "What's the matter,
Roger? What is it? I simply—"

"*You simply!*" he said in that low, tight voice she had heard
only once before. "Listen to me, Martha. You simply better
not mention that name again—not to me or anybody else in
this town—if you expect to leave it—in one piece—the last
of May."

Could she have been more astonished, more shocked? This
was the football player, Carrie's *spouse*, who was so taboo?
And hadn't she heard his name mentioned?—of course she
had, a number of times, and always in the most flattering
light. Except that—this did occur to her—it was true that not
only had she never heard his father's name cross Ray's lips,
but never once had she heard the other children speak of
him either. That meant nothing in itself; there might just
never have been the occasion. Still . . . "the flattering light"
. . . was she so much a part of things, so initiated and at-
tuned to the town's inner workings as to be the best judge of
innuendo, or irony, or secret jokes? There had been *something*, the undefinable mystery, or she would not have sought
out Roger.

She let the matter drop, not so much out of cowardice as
through default: whom else could she approach? But she was
worried, bothered. What if she had miscalculated the com-
plexity of Ray's suffering? What if this father, far from standing for glorified conformity, the hero whose shoes were too
big for his son to fill, as she had supposed, stood instead for
—for what? Who was Harry Hibbard? Peegram Hero? Peegram's Aaron Burr or Benedict Arnold? *If you expect to*

leave it in one piece. That expression on Roger's face! Her ignorance the stranger's ignorance. Sometimes it seemed like the last bitter dregs in the bottom of the cup after the poison has already been swallowed.

7

Yesterday—the day of the ball game—Martha's room was in a merry mood, Martha too. Ball games were tremendous events in Peegram and school was to let out at noon. Many stores would close; the whole town would turn out. It was both comforting and reassuring to remember there were other things in this world besides the race problem. For the first time, Martha felt scaled to size again, somewhat herself again, somewhat free of the oppressive weight of recent happenings and free of the fantasying her love entailed. It might have been the first day the class felt free too. Even Ray's half-sleeping state seemed overlaid with an excitement. Martha found herself thinking—and this while she was not planning to go—Thank God for ball games. What would we do without them? It was good—good!—to be gay.

The children were so keyed up that, the last fifteen minutes before the noon bell, Martha was hard pressed. They put their books away, picked up papers, readied and steadied themselves for departure, and still there were these fifteen endless minutes left. Current Events, what they had used to get through last minutes so handily with, had that special and direful connotation. Besides, there was only one event today, praise the Lord—the game. So, Martha said, bethinking herself, why not discuss, during these last fifteen intolerable minutes, what they would like to be when they grew up? There was a flicker of interest, an instant daubing of the proposed subject with the holiday spirit. Lester said he would be a banker, so that he would never lack for cash. (They all laughed.) Louise Pierce said she would be a model because she had red hair and green eyes and what more could you ask? Tad was going to be a peanut farmer. And since Tad, as everybody knew, could eat his weight in peanuts any old time, that seemed a happy enough choice; the children approved.

Martha had not intended calling on Ray, or taking the least chance—today—on those unpredictable tears they all dreaded. When she saw his hand go up, she thought, Why, he never has raised his hand before, never has volunteered. (He had not raised his hand for permission to speak on folks and dogs—that had come wrenched out of him, with no preceding formalities.) She had hesitated before saying, "Yes, Ray?"

And again he was standing up, which was not their custom, and again the bell was about to ring. (Afterward, she wondered whether the memory of this curious repeat on "the other time" remained in minds other than hers. *He that spoke but now is no longer in the room.* Only twice was he to unburden himself in words. And they did not know, nobody could have foretold . . . that a sparrow would fly too low.) He was standing there, with the remaining minutes of the intolerable fifteen minutes the gift they gave to him, wrapping him round, but at first words failed him, and they were conscious that there was no more time (because the bell would ring) and a wave of restlessness went over the room.

Ray said, "I'm going to be a football player. All-American."

Frail, flimsy child. What could be more patently ridiculous? But not a ripple, not a thread of laughter answered him. There was silence.

Ray said—and there were no tears; his voice ascended another step—"I'll be a baseball player too."

Just as ridiculous. Not a sound from the room. The silence deepening as the clear, bell-like voice climbed.

"And a furniture salesman," Ray said.

Surely that was all: the voice could climb no higher, it had reached some promontory, while the silence could sink to no more impenetrable depths.

"I—I'll be for liberty and justice for all, black and white. . . . *I'll be like my dad.*"

Her skin prickled, hearing "liberty and justice for all," the last words of "I Pledge Allegiance" coming back at her like this. Then she was aware that the silence did not give; there was not one crack in it; it was absolute. A wall. The name that had crossed those lips at last was thrown back. Nor was this children's cruelty. Children's cruelty would have dictated derision and laughter—that Ray, who among them was the least good at sports, should entertain such fancies. Children's cruelty would have been a blessing, by comparison. This was something else, older and more unyielding than they were—rejection, unwilled, not to be got around. It seemed to run as deep and common to them all as when they had frozen solid against her for taking her stand on segregation. "Liberty and justice for all, *black and white.*" Something seemed to click into place inside her. . . . The summit of the dream was reached, the dreamer poised and trembling there for his release, his period of mourning accomplished, as it were; his plea now in the clear, awaiting the permission derision would have granted: "Yes, we know, we know, your father was a big athlete and a fine man, and you're such a screw, such a cut-down squirt, you couldn't be like him in a million years. What a laugh. You might as well decide to be yourself." Because he was ready, because he had made it explicit. Even as he said, "I'm going to be a football player," ready not to be; even as he affirmed "I'll be like my dad," able to move into his very different self—that which is easily understood when it's in code, and providing the derision is directed against the self and not the father. It's the father who *must* be accepted, when the son has been in mourning for so long. Whereupon there is a bridge (a suspension bridge, perhaps) from the dream's summit, which has to be climbed first, back to life again. What Martha had been hoping for, waiting for all year. But the father was not accepted—black and white; the other time, black and white and spotted dogs—oh no, it couldn't be. But *Taboo*, the silence screamed, *his father was unclean*. The rejection and its finality. The terrible crime of which the father was guilty written in black and white—what else? why else? The impression of "the other time" stamped all over this one, the one spring that could produce . . . She stood there, staring. Ray worshiping that which he, even as the son, had permission only to revile? What else could make the children unable, in any sort of code at all, to let Harry Hibbard be properly mourned and properly buried by his son? More lonely than loneliness was Ray's fate, in this case. A stranger was well off.

Ray had not sat down.

It seemed incomprehensible when she would have said
that all year the children had taken Ray under their special
protection; that, by definition, Ray belonged peculiarly to
them. They took care of him, hitting him to give him legiti-
mate reason for his tears, again and again attracting his
attention to keep him the safe side of his dream (to keep him
waked up enough so he could navigate), tacitly taking him
over from a mother who did everything for him but love
him; developing a fairly elaborate code. Martha would have
said—she would have staked a lot on it—it was these children who had kept Ray this side of a mental illness that
would have shocked the good people of Peegram speechless
(and in a child of eleven). So they betrayed him when the
time came. (How utterly alone he seemed.) No, it was not
to be fathomed. When they were the ones who had nurtured
him, could they be the ones to commit him to a term of life
imprisonment with his dream? She had the terrible certainty
that though they had all known how short it was to be, this
life term, they still could not have shown mercy. My God.
In the absoluteness of their own rejection, they seemed helpless.

Black and white; rebellion and defeat. The connection between her and Ray proving to be both deeper and more
separate than she could have imagined in her wildest flights.
Maybe she was mad, completely thrown off by recent happenings. But if Ray, unlike herself, the stranger, was repeating rebellion and defeat "in the blood," from within—ah, it
cast a strange new light over Peegram, made her want to
know as she never had.

The bell rang. In desperation, she asked Ray to stay a few
minutes and help her erase the boards. Desperately she

tried to get through, to say it in code: "Your father must have . . ." (Your father must have been a fine man), but her word carried no weight against their rejection, she was a stranger here herself, she didn't *know*. He left her, dreaming. ("Can I go now, Miss L?")

She paid her debt in failure, and the failure was hers, dead center, where she lived. Released, he might have opened his eyes and seen the foul ball coming his way. He might have ducked in time, he might not have been killed. Now, the tragedy was knocked home before he ever went there. A baseball. Her earlier anger, that it should have been a *baseball* as the modern mocking counterpart of the Fates, of the blind Fury with the abhorred shears, slitting the thin-spun life, left her. Her own part was so much worse. She— and the children—would always remember, even in all the embroidery of forgetting, what had happened first. (The bird, at least, was in passage.)

I hadn't failed as a teacher, Martha thought. It was about all I had left.

To teach is to love? But to teach is to meet the odd off-beat moments when a soul seeks liberating. To drop the one word now, or then, in the mind that's ready for it, that which it is not usually given to parents to do. A fragile, sacred province.

And if—now—whatever happened happened around Ray, because of his fame, because of his speech about folks and dogs and perhaps with "liberty and justice for all, black and white" thrown in, and with whatever of the past that might be moiling up, it would still be an irony incidental to tragedy, always. In Martha's heart.

8

It was not until this morning—when Roger came for her—
that she had learned the news of Ray's death, although last
evening Mr. Josiah had told her he had got hit, but not hurt,
he had added with a greedy leer, got off lighter than that
there bird. Some sight, that bird; he allowed as how he had
never seen the like. Right scary. Smack. Slick as a whistle.
Red, he said, whoever Red was, was might near put off his
game, but Tom Carter picked the critter up by one leg and
flung it over the fence, so that Martha found herself imagining it there in its final resting place, in no shoe-box coffin and
with no spoon-dug grave to mark it. (She was a little girl of
many bird funerals herself.)

Roger had told her about Ray, as they were driving to the
school. He said he would have called her in the night, had
she had her own telephone. Carrie had called him about midnight, he said. He said very few people had seen the ball
actually hit Ray; he himself had not; it was the way the sun
was shining straight in their eyes. But some who had seen it
claimed that the boy had got flustered—rattled. They saw
William Morrison disappearing through the school doors just
as they drove up and Roger said that was odd, William Morrison coming to school this first day after his cousin's death;
it was contrary to custom, he said. At the game, Ray and
William Morrison had been sitting together, he said.

When Martha reached her room, the bell had already rung
and the children were in their places. One sidelong look was
enough to tell her that they knew—probably, like herself,

most of them had just heard. Ray's empty desk was the one
fact that could and did speak. There was nothing to say, but
neither could they proceed as though nothing had happened.
Death does not happen, Martha thought. A first experience
with death is an experience with nothing at all, and for most
of the children this would be a first experience of death with
somebody their own age. Their eyes moved from Ray's desk
to Martha's face and veered away: *tell us.* There is nothing
to tell. Like his dad, he is not anywhere. William Morrison's
face was wooden; his face alarmed her. (His capacity for
loving had always alarmed her.) It occurred to her, as a side
thought, that William Morrison could not boss death and that
that realization might shock him very much.

Martha said, "Ray stayed in a little while yesterday after
the bell rang. I asked him to, remember? I . . . asked him
to erase the boards. The last thing he said in here was, 'Can
I go now, Miss L?'" She sensed their relief. Somehow, she
had stumbled on the right thing, the right epitaph, and it
ought to be carved on his headstone, *Can I go now, Miss L?*
They could remember him (and, oddly, did remember him)
by that. They felt her veracity; felt she had quoted him
exactly. They saw him ascending heavenward in a white
cloud of chalk dust. Louise Pierce said, "And what did you
say, Miss L?" They waited tensely.

"I said, 'Yes, dear.'" They nodded—this was ineffably right
and fitting. Then Martha said (because she thought she
must, because she had the notion one must always try not
to dodge reality, particularly when it came to children, and
because a drama had been played out in here), "We all
know—I expect we have occasion to know it better than
almost anybody else—how Ray felt about his dad . . ." As

wrong as the other had been right—they would not have it, this violation of taboo, this treading where angels must not. She stared at them helplessly; they stared helplessly back at her. (All but William Morrison, whose eyes were quite sightless.) She bowed her head; they bowed theirs. The Lord's Prayer came out in shaky unison. Then, in yet shakier unison, with considerable stumbling over the last words, "I Pledge Allegiance."

Although William Morrison kept wide of her on the playground at both the morning and afternoon recess periods, he hung around at the noon hour and again after the 3:20 bell. Heavy in him were words that would not come. But apparently he found no opening and would not allow Martha to provide him with one. As stiff as a wooden soldier, he erased everything on every one of the boards, including all the grammar sentences they were to take up Monday. Martha would not have thought of stopping him.

Steps on the stairs, loud and measured. Involuntarily, Martha looked at her watch: nine o'clock, almost to the minute. She would have said it was much later, midnight at least. The breeze scooped up a shade and dropped it with a thump. What did she suppose—that the only entrance was by way of the window, through which the rock never should have sailed with such ease had not the screen been rotten? The steps came on and stopped at the other side of her door. That these particular steps did not belong to the household she was aware, that they were not Mrs. Josiah's weasel ones or Mr. Josiah's bullish ones—this was clear. They were irreducible, these were. There was a knock. She stared distractedly at the open roll book, at the newspaper clipping on

the table in front of her, but made no move to shunt them
into the drawer. The knock was repeated. "May I come in?"
asked a deep and resonant woman's voice. "Come in," was
her reply.

There stood Carrie Hibbard—calm, massive. Not fat, but
big and foursquare. (There was really only the one word—
massive—to describe her.) Of course, Martha thought, she
would always come up steps exactly as she has—she would
not deviate, coming faster or slower—and one would learn
that after a while. But she was rather surprised to note the
handsome, regular features, the healthy brown hair, the
smooth sweep of the forehead, the straight nose and the tidy
mouth. No nonsense here. Good bones under good solid
flesh. Undisposed ever to decay. She could be any age and
triumph. (Only, what mortal man would have dared to pre-
sume?) And because she must never have been young, she
would never be old. Why had not more women settled it in
the same way? Carrie was not one of the parents Martha had
visited, though she had sent her notes once or twice. And
why hadn't she done so, when Ray had been maybe her
chiefest problem? Because. Because she had been so sure she
could expect no help from this quarter.

While Martha stood up, neither Carrie nor Martha spoke.
Neither accused. If Carrie saw the clipping or the roll book,
she gave no sign. Hysteria riffled the packed-down, salted-
down silence. Martha wanted desperately to speak of the
bird. Wasn't it *funny* about the bird, tee-hee. A giggle was
high in her throat. Besides, she liked this woman, and it was
not a discovery she would have cared to make at this
moment.

Carrie said, "As you do not make a habit of going to

church, you probably do not intend going tomorrow since it is to be in the church. I have simply come to make sure."

"To the funeral?" Martha asked, with the giggle not altogether absent from her voice. (And was Dr. Erwin conducting the service? Who else?)

"Yes, to his funeral," Carrie said, looking off over Martha's head. "We could not locate a casket to fit him—the casket's much too big."

"Ah—so," Martha said.

"But I have come to make sure—that is, to ask that you do not attend the funeral on any account."

"Ah—so," Martha wanted to say again, but checked herself.

Carrie said, "To speak plainly, it would not be wise."

By a great effort Martha collected her wits—became sober —put the bird firmly out of her mind.

Carrie said, "The mood and temper of the town right now, it's important we don't court trouble—it will just be safer if you stay away."

"I see," Martha said slowly. "Yes, I think I understand." She paused. "I'm not much for funerals. Ordinarily, I'd be glad to oblige you. But—"

"So many people will be there," Carrie said. "Parents and . . . all sorts. In our town everybody goes to funerals, Miss Lyerly. Surely you understand that lately we have taken every precaution to avoid gatherings. This one tomorrow cannot be avoided, don't you see, and you must stay away."

Martha said, "My contract does not expire until May thirtieth, Mrs. Hibbard. Until then, I'm my children's teacher. A number of them will be at the funeral—you've just told me as much. It's for their sake that I'll be present too. They wouldn't understand if I didn't go. I'm sorry—I have to be there."

Carrie said, "It's for your own sake I'm asking you not to come."

"I realize that and I'm sorry I can't comply."

The beautiful (because it was a beautiful) and unfumbling voice continued, "You can't know what you're doing."

"No," Martha said, wondering at her courage. "Only what I have to do."

"Think it over," Carrie said, turning away unhurriedly. "You have the whole night in which to change your mind."

She was gone: the steps sounding down the stairs.

Seth Erwin

1

NINE-THIRTY. THE SERVICE WAS TO BEGIN AT TEN. IT WAS NOT unusual for him to be in his church study half an hour early; it was very nearly his habit. But this morning he was not going over sermon notes one last time, experiencing, like some prima donna before curtain time, that direful interval of self-annihilation. This morning he was sitting on the edge of his desk, with arms tightly folded across his breast, facing the door and waiting. From outside there could already be heard the occasional slamming of a car door, the muffled sound of steps; no voices as yet.

Discreetly placed at one side of the door was a small walnut-framed mirror. He was not the one who had thought to hang it there—obviously, it was meant to take a last look in, to be sure that no dandruff clung to the collar and that the tie had not gone askew. Seth seldom bothered with the mirror; he knew himself too well to have to make such last-minute appraisals. He was one of those mortals unvisited by minor miscalculations and disasters—he did not have dandruff. But sitting the way he was now, he was confronting his face in the mirror; noting the small, localized, yet absolute frown that ran vertically from somewhere below mid-point of his hairline down his forehead and ending at the bridge of his nose. It was a frown that was perpetual now, he supposed; completely characteristic of him. It was a fine face, all the same. He knew. He had read enough, and compared enough, to know. Capitalized on it enough, bartered it often enough. As a face, it pleased him. He had come across it (this face) for the first time, he remembered, when he was about five years old, in the old unused front parlor of Aunt Phoebe's and Aunt Deb's old wreck of a house, towered and gabled and fretted with wooden lace, and with those narrow slits of stained glass windows, cathedral windows (how he had developed a fondness for going to the bathroom there and finding himself bathed in celestial light); the house rotting away at such a rate that it seemed pitched at an acute angle, the wooden lace coming to pieces in patches, hanging and dangling and banging in the slightest wind, so that it must have been the suppressed desire of more than one passer-by, as well as his own, to be able to pick it off, like a scab; the house dying out from under the two old maid Erwin sisters, Aunt Phoebe and Aunt Deb, who must finally have set it afire, committing it—and themselves—to hell one clear and moony night. It was in the dim old parlor, smelling of dust and leather, stiff in furniture, deep in slab-top tables of the ponderous and intricate legs, themselves overpowered by

the great secretary, further dignified by its load of china
shepherdesses and iron dogs (on point, with creneled tails
held iron-taut), and Napoleon's bust, and a snow man with
a whole snow storm in a round glass globe that could not
be reached by a boy to turn upside down and set the snow
snowing once more; the silk tasseled-and-fringed lamps, the
glass spangled lamps sitting around like ghosts, hatted and
gloved—it was here where most of the old Erwin portraits
hung, the Erwins being a family who, like the Egyptian
kings, believed in leaving testimonials. It was here Seth first
encountered his face. He had looked a long while at the
black, silver-buckled shoes and the black stockings below
the tight black broadcloth knee breeches, the buff waistcoat
under the bottle-green tail coat and the high white stock
rising to the face that was his own. "That's me," he said,
probably later, when he was bolder in his discovery. Aunt
Phoebe had laughed and said, "Well, that's Seth, all right." It
was not particularly reassuring, since even when he was five,
Seth had known Aunt Phoebe was moldering in old virginity.

But Seth, the son of Zebulon, the son of Seth . . . forever
and ever. He had stopped that, he had broken that chain. His
son was not Zebulon but William Morrison, named after his
wife Elaine's father, old William Morrison of Madison, a
"Morrison of Madison" even as he was "an Erwin of Peegram." A sacrilege that still caused him to catch his breath
sometimes. How had he dared? And was it the beginning of
the end of all revolt then? Or was it that he pronounced
himself the last of the Erwins? Because the Erwins had not,
until Seth came along, produced any preachers. Near everything else, millers and wheelwrights and harness makers and
horse traders and doctors and lawyers and gentlemen farmers

and statesmen, but no preachers. No, the Erwins were a more portrait-sitting than God-fearing family. In good style and fitting boldness, the Erwins had worshiped themselves. Not that they hadn't amply and generously allowed for failures and ne'er-do-wells in every generation—consider the harness makers, the millers—but never never had the eldest—the Seth or the Zebulon—failed, as Seth had, and by negligent willfulness, to pass on the sacred name and all that it implied. Still, by way of the small walnut-framed mirror, Seth must come back at himself with a thin, ironic smile: the rebel, the rebel without dandruff. He could not just say that the rebel had made such a smashing success of, for instance, breaking with the tradition of the type of woman the Erwin male joined himself to, in holy matrimony—the Ruth type, the "thy people shall be my people and thy God my God" type; the type who gleans little dibs and dabs of what the master does not require for his own gross needs, who snuggles at the master's feet; that which had made for such amiable perpetuation of the Erwin stamp. Because for all that careful underlining of "Morrison," Elaine was a slave. It was not recorded, Boaz's boredom.

For a male Erwin in the line of succession this added middle name was so glaringly evident, was so shocking, as to stop even the child's playmates from dropping it out, or condensing the whole into "Bill." How did William Morrison Erwin like it? Did he understand yet how, in adding, his father had in fact cut him off? (When in happier frame of mind, Seth would tell himself he had done this in order to liberate his son; to give him a chance to escape the iron heel of the past.) I have broken it for *all* time. William Morrison cannot name his son Seth and *continue* anything or *be* anything except foolish. What's in a name? In a title? —In Chairman of the Junior Citizens' Committee? The mirror told him that he did not reply even with the thin ironic smile. *His* son was dead, was laid out in a casket that did not fit him. *His* son whom he had not known, but recognized in certain crevices of his being. But when the foul ball had arced its course across the sun and he, suddenly on his feet, suddenly straining toward prayer—he had seen them both, William Morrison and Ray, side by each on the bench, with the ball driving down—his heart vomiting upward and blinding him until after the ball had made its selection. It was the only time I have ever loved him.

Long ago, it was Seth's own mordant ambition that had frightened him so. Long ago, he had sat watching another game, a football game, in a university stadium. It was a very critical game, with a Southern Conference championship title, or some such thing, hanging in the balance. The score was tied up, he recalled; the score was seven to seven. In the last minutes of play of the last quarter, the ball was snapped to one, Harry Hibbard, who, swinging around left end, began to run—was it forty yards, sixty yards?—for a touchdown. Then the scene becomes confused, because everybody is spilling over into the field, wildly cheering, and it is as if the winter sky is blown into fragments. The goal posts go crashing down. Darkness comes. There are torches, a triumphant procession across the campus, with Harry Hibbard sitting high on shoulders of adorers. There are songs, but the songs keep being interrupted by fresh outbreaks of the same violent cheering. It will never end. Seth follows along, chafing his hands and crying—what kind of tears he does not ask, for it is bitter cold. It is this night he feels the call to become a preacher, he feels the icy hand of God seize his heart; that is why he remembers it etched in its entirety inside him. He is lying prostrate on his bed when Harry comes in. They are roommates, although during the football season Harry does not sleep at the fraternity house. Still, he comes in, his face quiet and tired. He nods to Seth and Seth sits up. Seth says the correct things, but Seth is jealous because the other face is not involved. It is remote from it all and sad. . . .

Once Seth put his hand to the plow, he did not look back. Not so much the discovery that he needed those wild, redundant cheers for himself, as his despising of himself for needing them. And when Harry could have done without! When Harry seemed to think of them as a kind of punishment he did not fully understand the necessity for. Around the fraternity house they were referred to as B. and B., Brain and Brawn. Between them, a sort of pitting of *the word* against *the deed*, although it was doubtful whether Harry ever realized there was, between them, any conflict. Harry was so humble, so respecting of Seth's mind, an attitude which provoked Seth's secret laughter, since Harry's own mind, while un-meteorlike, was probably better. Anyhow, Seth knew full well he would have to *talk* his way to fame if he was to achieve it at all. And Seth was sick of the endless stereotyped fantasy productions where he—Seth—was nursing a pigskin and stiff-arming his way, weaving and dodging his way, a gallant and solitary figure of pure power in an empty field, achieving thus his immortality, while the sky fell to the tune of thunderous cheers. Seth had to be purged. And, ah yes, he did have the gift of words and a golden voice to fall back on—"the Erwin voice"—which had already made one United States Senator and two Congressmen and a number of state legislators, and which would have made a governor too had not Seth's great-grandfather died at the head of his regiment at Chancellorsville; but no preachers!

In seminary, Seth had for a time slept on a board and practiced self-flagellation. He had (this was another phase) worn an amethyst necklace constantly under his shirt and anointed himself with perfume from a fluted, fan-shaped bottle with an elongated stopper. *Toujours Moi?* He had forgotten. He had, in long hours in the library, in poring over all those great dark tomes as required, taken to illuminating text and margin with obscenities. If upon reading "We are thus confronted with the age-old question: what is man?" striking through *age-old*, inserting *old-age*, and feeling tremendous gratification. And yet more gratification when he understood his fantasy productions had indeed undergone alterations. He could now fantasy himself achieving his immortality, making his magnificent contribution to truth by traveling all over the world, from great library to great library, and inscribing the great and solemn books with obscenities for posterity to come upon and reckon with. He could hear the cheers. He had another favorite sport, a word game. He collected words like *sneers* and *cheers, impotence* and *importance, womb* and *tomb,* setting them up as silent partners, brooding over the womb-tomb difference of a letter. Then he read that in many ancient languages—in Egyptian and Sanskrit and Arabic and even in Latin—opposites were frequently designated by the *same* word. This was the ticket, *tomb* and *tomb.* In seminary, Seth came off with honors, first in his class, and formally designated, in the final exercises, as the seminary's white hope. His eloquence astonished; his orthodoxy most satisfactorily underscored nearly two thousand years of being

sure. Never once had Seth raised his voice in doubt or dis-
agreement with the professor of dogmatic theology, or the
professor of Old Testament logic, or the professor of Christian ethics, or the professor of pastoral behavior, or any
professor whatsoever.

All of which was long ago (long enough ago).

By stages, Seth had made his way back to Peegram. A war
came first. Fresh out of seminary, he was a chaplain, in rather
the same category with the mascot, the puppy with the patch
over the eye and the bright red tongue and the persistently
bright eye—not perhaps as altogether meaningful as the mascot or as provocative of luxury sentiments, the Protestant
Man of God in a war, but nevertheless . . . cute and roguish
enough, with his "Thou shalt not kill" crisscrossed with his
"Be not afraid, boys, God is on our side." Seth had helped the
medics when he could. "Hello, chappie," one youngster had
said, when he was breathing his last. "Don't take no wooden
nickels." "You want me to pray for you?" Seth had asked.
"No, chappie," the boy got out at last, breaking the bloody
bubble that was forming over his mouth. "If you gotta pray,
pray for God." "O.K.," Seth said; he was, by that time,
closing the eyes. . . .

But Harry, now. In football, Harry was a halfback. In
baseball, he was a pitcher. Breaking precedent at the university by playing both. Baseball coach screaming he would
ruin his pitching arm in football. Football coach screaming
he would ruin his back—or was it his knee?—in baseball.
Both trying to nail him with the scholarship that would
have committed him. And he, with that hard-to-define
sadness about him, keeping his distance, placating both,
contending he was not good enough at either, rather than

too good at each, to make the choice, all this while making All-American and dodging the big-league scouts who were after him. It was enough to make you sick. Then, in the war. In the war, Harry was in the Air Corps (Air Corps, not Air Force in those days); not some greasy member of a ground crew, but a fly boy, a fighter pilot, *bona fide*, who shot down so many Germans that his picture appeared in the papers and medals were prescribed.

The last stage on Seth's way back to Peegram was the much larger First Church at Lewisville, which he had given up when the Peegram Pulpit Committee had approached him with its offer. Harry had come back too, by that time, and Carrie had never left. His own honeymoon with Elaine was over. He could not say it had ever blossomed lavishly; yet there had been, for a while, a shy and tentative bloom. But the night he had asked her in a whisper what thoughts went through her mind when they were making love and she had replied, meekly and thoughtfully, herself a little frightened, a little surprised, "Why, Seth. I guess I nearly always plan the next day's menus"—after that night, he was free.

Elaine did not know, no one knew, of his present debaucheries. How he debauched over into music, into art, into the reading of poetry and literature. The annual trip he made to New York, where he went, not only to get his suits, or his ties by Sulka, but where he also went from gallery to gallery, from concert to concert, looking always furtively over his shoulder to be sure he was not followed. Where he bought the books and the records he had shipped back and that did not appear either in this study or the one in the parsonage. He was ashamed! In the amount of guilt generated, the amethyst necklace had not stirred up a tenth of what he felt now over this present sin. Plain-back novels and French postcards would not be able to touch it.

Under Seth, church membership had increased some thirty per cent and there was no longer any organized church dissension. The Building Fund was bursting at the seams, with nearly half a million dollars in it, so that it wouldn't be long before they could break ground for the new church. The young people's program was thriving, the choirs now numbered three instead of one. (Of course, as some few were wont to point out, Seth had Carrie behind him.) He never threw it back to the good people, that when he spoke at conferences and assemblies and other churches (where he was in considerable demand) he was called great and had been made offers—by Madison, by Gate City, big churches; by one church as far away as St. Louis—these offers of which his board of deacons inevitably heard, but which he never took up.

Outside the pulpit, his function, as he had come to define it, was to listen. And it was curious what a concentrated function it had turned out to be. Not that he was exactly detached, or disinterested, or even that he had made himself into an appropriate vessel into which people felt safe emptying their emotional garbage, but as if compelled out of some cold depths of tenderness peculiar to him to take it all in and (although they did not realize the importance of this) suspend judgment. He made his pastoral calls assiduously —made the rounds of the sick and the aged and the ones in trouble and the potential new members—he devoted two days a week to this. Then there was the stream of those who made their way to this study where he also kept regular hours. It was especially interesting, he thought, when he never gave out advice and was not yet, at least, a hander out of cards of "how to's," never summoned the Almighty to his side. Listened. So that his estimate of human loneliness was different from what it had used to be, when he had rather thought the sensitive and the intelligent held the monopoly.

Seth did not gossip.

Seth did not smoke or drink.

Seth did not succumb to women.

With his name and his wardrobe (the way his trousers broke over his shoes was a wonder to behold!) and with his big (although carefully conservative) car, with his wife and his private income and his pristine private life, with that elegance about him that he could not, if he had wanted to, get rid of—was it that he nevertheless entertained some vision of the camel's-hair shirt under the Brooks Brothers suit? Had he ever identified with the young Milton (so pretty that his school fellows had labeled him "Girlie")— being desirous of priestly fame? And if it had always been, despite the football and *etcetera* daydreams, despite (or because of) all the experiments in sin, a priestly fame he had hankered after? Having visions of justifying the ways of Man to man; of founding a new religion; of (later) revamping the old from within? But if he had had to have such fame, there was still that fastidious side of his nature, plus the particular quality of his intelligence, plus (perhaps) his fear of insanity, which forbade on every front, was there not? Which shook with shriveling laughter. And which, without mercy, dictated his return to the spot where he was born and reared (a dog returns to its vomit), there forcing him to sustain dressed-up failure ("failure with success") as its surrogate. And was it, then, by way of punishment and atonement, imposed by himself, upon himself, for as long as he should draw breath? It was hard to tell. He himself was not sure and nobody else had ever prized him open. It was as if his exterior were too perfect for any such meddling. And there was the odd self-sufficiency about him too. Self-flagellation, the wearing of the necklace had not required co-operation from any other. They were performed alone and in secret. Never, at his most desperate, had Seth gone whoring.

Last summer, almost coinciding in time with Harry Hibbard's drowning (and Harry Hibbard had gone out and, as the initiated knew, if insurance adjusters and outsiders did not, deliberately drowned himself), Peegram's Chamber of Commerce had voted Seth Erwin its Man of the Year. That came rather hard, it hit Seth rather hard. The last illusion of hair shirt gone maybe? Cheers, maybe? For what he had recommended, in the way of prayer rooms and such, out at Royall Furniture, to keep the union out? Or the reward for his splendid co-operation with Carrie, all these years, culminating as it had in a friend's defeat and drowning? This while he would still have been nourishing the notion of himself as sinister, as a warning not altogether devoid of moral meaning? But when it would seem that what he had done had after all provoked only his own solitary shudder and instinctive withdrawal, and cheers. Was he then, *without irony,* their boy? (Or their mascot?) The marks of the world, the badges of success he wore—to

mock them, as he would have supposed—causing them only
to conclude complacently (if they had sensed, for all these
marks and badges, he wasn't worldly a bit; *they* knew he
owned no shares of Royall stock but, oh God, they also knew
who did!) that it was his name and the security of money
left to him in trust which made him so fascinatingly immune
and so acceptable to them. The laurels he would have worn
as thorns turning out to be laurels, in fact. Who was there
to condemn? To call him evil? Name him hypocrite? He was
beautiful to them.

In a small town, he did cut rather a strange figure, being
certainly more the figure of fashion and breeding than good
shepherd herding his sheep. Perhaps, therefore, neither
they nor he quite understood that what he really filled for
them was the role of "tragic figure." That what they liked
best about him was his renunciation. Moved, because they
had trapped him and because he could never get away
again; would never find himself, and was after all so im-
peccable in despair. (They should have allowed him—well,
if not Bartok, then certainly Beethoven, had they guessed
his sin.) And when he stood in the pulpit—what he had
least understanding of—he was curiously pure, with a cold
purity of passion, as if seized and shaken by the Holy
Ghost. Almost never could his congregation remember what
he had said, afterward. (He couldn't either. For while he
prepared his sermons in advance, and with the utmost paid-
out care, he never used them as they were; they underwent
transformation.) They said vaguely that there wasn't *too*
much hellfire-damnation in these sermons. But he himself
thought of them as being like epileptic seizures—he had
long since ceased to trust them.

2

He raised his head and listened. The sounds of the slamming of car doors were more closely spaced now and beginning to overlap, one with another. Still no voices; but people's voices, before a funeral, were always subdued.

Seth's father, Zebulon Erwin, that proud bearer of the proud name, was the town's atheist and the town's windbag, a kind of "end of the affair" of the Erwin voice, it looked like, for a while. And it occurred to Seth that the town "afforded" him in much the same spirit it had "afforded" his father, as if allowing no particular difference between the town's atheist and the town's Man of God. Showing the same indulgence and the same imperviousness. Not that an Erwin could do no wrong, but that an Erwin could do neither right nor wrong, whatever he did. *Driven, derided, Father, and my will a curve.* Florid, sensual, bigoted (his father was exceedingly bigoted in his much-touted unbelief), with a pot for a belly from which issued those echoing guffaws, Seth's father sat with his feet up on his desk for forty years, shifting his weight enough, ever and anon, to hit the brass spittoon that he kept on in his office long after such receptacles went out of fashion and were pronounced repulsive. Wooden steps, with black rubber treads, led up to this office where the door stood always open and where there were never fewer than three courthouse bums keeping his father company, listening to his father expound. His father's law practice was largely a myth, as Seth early discovered, which everybody, including his mother, sup-

ported. Improvidence and laziness were never held up to
Zebulon. That sense of his own importance continued un-
nicked by the slightest sense of failure all the years of his
life. (When, toward the end, he had started taking heroin,
its purpose was not to help him escape any feelings of failure
but to add the warm and rosy glow, to round out success
as the slightly aging lover of his dead brother's widow; also,
since quite incidentally he and the widow were playing
ducks and drakes with the dead brother's quite impressive
estate, a little special glow of forgetting was what the doctor
ordered, so to speak.) Zebulon did go, one term, to the state
legislature and swap stories with the boys there. The state
legislature was not supposed to be able to convene without
an Erwin answering the roll call. And Erwin County stood
ready to elect him as its representative again and again, had
he just been able to stir himself enough to run. He was not
perturbed when Seth's mother died of pellagra, although
his brother Abel (Carrie's father, the one whose widow,
which is to say, Carrie's mother, he was later to cavort with)
roared with rage; claimed the family was in disgrace.

Seth remembered his father as a loosely fleshed man, wearing (always) the same widely spaced, black-striped shirt
with the unclean and wilted collar and satin tie, spotted with
food and grease; pants riding low on loose hips, and fly
almost never closed, so that Seth's mother, who called him
"Mr. Erwin," after the old ways, would say "Mr. Erwin,"
in that special tone reserved for tactfully reminding. Seth's
most vivid mental picture of his father showed him prodding
Seth with a swollen forefinger and calling him "Sethie Boy,"
prior to loading Seth's pockets with sourballs. Affection.

Seth did not think it was so surprising that his uncle Abel

more or less adopted him. Abel was the money-making genius, the founder of Royall Furniture, and he had no son of his own, only Carrie. He could "afford" Seth! It was Abel who sent Seth off to college in style, and to the seminary too, though this latter he considered poppycock. It was Abel who provided so handsomely for Seth in his will, ironically enough a provision which his father, as executor, hadn't been able to touch, while playing through the widow Flora's share; in other words, the very nearly everything that was earmarked for Carrie, which was to go intact to Carrie at Flora's death; Royall Furniture was what Abel had intended to leave to Carrie. That she had not got it in the way Abel intended must have something to do with something, Seth thought with a grimace. That, therein, hung a tale. But he did not pursue it. Instead, he was remembering his mother, her last years, hiding—caching away—bits of candy in odd boxes and chests and the dark corners of the drawers of bureaus. No wonder the mice were so attentive. Seth was glad when he could offer the wretched old house to the town as a museum. Much older than Aunt Phoebe's and Aunt Deb's house, it was built in 1786 for some of the "town" Erwins and taken over by Seth's great-grandmother after the Civil War when Rosehill, "the Erwin place" (their plantation, although never so-called in these parts), was burned—not by General Stoneman's troops and not by Kirk's raiders but, there were those who allowed, by Erwin slaves.

Seth had not moved from his desk. He was still sitting with arms folded when he heard the rapid, bumbling steps coming down the hall. Jesse coming. Jesse Tate. (The Tates and the McDowells and the Averys were the "other" families of Peegram.) Jesse was chairman of Seth's board of deacons, about sixty years old, president of the First National Bank, and a good sort, reminding Seth of Peter. One could easily fancy him betraying three times before the cock crew and then crying his eyes out. He had his rocklike attributes too. Increasingly Seth relied on him, because unlike certain of the other deacons he was not merely and only Carrie's front boy. He respected her but without going under.

His hasty knock, his hurling the door open before Seth had time to say "Come in"—these were exactly like him. When he was upset, he proclaimed it from the housetop; he let you know about it, bless him.

"Hello, Jess."

"Cool as a cucumber!" Jesse cried.

Seth very nearly closed his eyes.

"Ten minutes to ten, Seth."

"Yes, I know. I know, Jess. I'm ready."

"You're ready! What are you so ready for?" He whipped out his handkerchief and gave his face the Turkish towel treatment. He backed up against the door, and when he had his breath under control, he said more quietly, "Things aren't good out there, Seth. I'm telling you and *been trying* to tell you! Carrie called you last night too. Told me so."

Seth unfolded his arms. "Both you and Carrie surprise me," he said. "Hysteria's not like Carrie, anyhow. Nothing is going to happen at a *funeral,* my good old friend. And nothing is going to happen in my church. And I'm not going to have any policemen standing around, hefting their holsters and defaming the place. That's final. And if I may say so, that's the worst idea either you or Carrie ever had."

Seth saw that Jesse winced.

"*She's* out there," he said. "*She's* here—Miss Lyerly."

Seth was not caught off guard. How could he have been, when he had arrived at his study early, and sat so still, waiting, reconnoitering, rehearsing the sense of himself, so that he could have it ready, like armor, in exactly the event that she did come here. "So what?" he was able to say coolly to Jess.

"So she didn't change her mind after Carrie gave her every chance and made it very clear why she should, that's what. That's the first 'what.' The second is, there must be at least twenty children out there already."

Seth shrugged.

"Kids all around. And somebody's going to get hurt. You think that's fine and dandy?"

"I just do not believe anybody's going to get hurt, that's all."

"No? You haven't been out there, Seth. You haven't *seen*. All the riled-up, scared-up parents—listen! They don't like Miss Lyerly, they don't like her one bit. They think she's *you know*. Poor lady, to hear them tell it, she's put a hex and a curse on this town. She's the one sent the boy straight to hell in a state of damnation and atheism, and the Lord knows what, a witch, a regular limb of Satan. She's the one who's done it, as sure as if she'd hit him over the head herself. Excited, Seth. People aren't themselves. Real-down superstitious, a lot of them. First the bird and then the ball *in the last half of the ninth*—warning signs from God, to hear them; this wickedness must stop. I tell you, I don't like it out there a bit."

"It'll be all right," Seth said. "It's certainly quiet. I haven't heard a sound."

Jesse said, "Oh my God—excuse me for swearing, Seth—

it *is* quiet! I've never seen the beat of it. You ever been in
a storm center? A storm center's *mighty* quiet. Moiling and
boiling out there, and all of it held in as tight as a drum!
Yes, it's quiet."

Frantically Jesse inspected his watch. He looked at Seth.
"I haven't told you *anything* yet."

"Go ahead."

He lowered his voice. "Know that gang that hangs out at
Peegram Hardware? That bunch of toughs headed up by
Andy Boyd?"

"Yes."

"Well, seems like they saw her—Miss Lyerly—the other
day in Peegram Hardware. Seems like she got their blood
up when it was already up, what with all the talk going
the rounds." Jesse paused; he swallowed hard. "Look, Seth.
It isn't just that these toughs are with us this morning. For
one thing, it's the way they're sitting. They came in together
—in a body—but they aren't sitting together, they spread out.
And I'll tell you this. It may be 'hysteria,' like you say; my
imagination, I'll grant you; but I don't like the way their
coats fit them."

"What do you mean?"

"Tight—too tight."

"What do you mean?"

"I mean—I'm afraid I mean sawed-off guns."

Seth stared. "Oh, come!"

"I wish *that* was all, but it's not."

"Go on then."

Jesse's deeply seamed and mobile face changed expression
completely in the instant, became somber and brooding.
"Harry's funeral was nine months ago, Seth."

"That's right."

"That isn't long enough ago, is it, Seth?"

Seth did not flush, he was not the sort to flush.

Jesse said, "Or maybe you've forgotten how Carrie and you 'encouraged' Jim and Jimbo out of town shortly before *that* funeral came off?"

"Jim and Jimbo," Seth said stupidly. Jim, the father, nearly as light of skin as Seth was; the small son, Jimbo, black, and you didn't think, as black as . . . Jim and Jimbo.

"Remember?" Jesse said. "The Negroes Harry went to hell for?"

Seth flexed his hands.

Jesse said softly, "Seth, you see, that's one thing Carrie and I didn't foresee. Jim and Jimbo turning up again. For *this* funeral. Seth, boy, Jim and Jimbo are sitting out there in the church auditorium right now."

Seth did stare.

"The way I figure it, the colored people must have been doing their own share of talking."

"They don't want desegregation," Seth said impatiently.

"Maybe not and maybe a lot of 'em who have got to hang on to their jobs as our janitors and our maids have been doing a lot of double talk, have you thought of that? There're some who want it, you can bet your last cent. And they must have been hearing plenty about this row over the schoolteacher and us kicking her out for standing up for them. After all, Madison's only forty-five miles from here and that's where Jim's been keeping himself—don't worry, he's been in touch! And he hasn't come back to attend any picnic, Seth. I don't 'spect he very much cared for what

happened to him. If we were burying that little boy out
there, simply as *Carrie's* son, that would be one thing.
But in view of the row over the teacher and in view of the
boy's last will and testament, as you might say, that spiel
about folks and dogs, and 'liberty and justice for all, black
and white' and with Jim sitting there in full sight . . . well,
what do you reckon? Is it Carrie's son or Harry's son we're
laying away? . . . No, wait.

"I told you, they don't like Miss Lyerly—they don't like
her looks or anything about her and she's the one sent the
boy straight to hell. But I'm telling you now, that with Jim
and Jimbo out there, it's like Harry's funeral was printed all
over this one. Harry did worse than she has, maybe, since
Harry was one of us, but it's like as if Harry had joined
forces with her through the boy. (Jim's out there.) And
. . . Carrie's son led astray—or Harry's son with Harry coming out in the blood—I tell you, either way she's hooked.
Harry's funeral wasn't long enough ago and you know it,
Seth! Hell, we know Harry killed himself and maybe we
know why, maybe because he wasn't going to be punished
by us—well, by the town; don't look like that. Anyway, he's
dead and can't be punished now. He's dead and the boy's
dead too, but *she's* not, Seth. *She's* come to church!"

Mopping his face, he went on. He told Seth that if he was
counting on those in the congregation who were merely
subdued and sorrowful over what had happened to hold
things down, he could forget about them. If he was counting on those who might be looking into their own hearts and
feeling none too good, he better forget about them too. If
they were out there at all, they weren't pulling together,
Jesse said—they were licking their own wounds and the

most they were asking for was not to have this business of segregation mixed up with death and souls and what not. He said maybe there were one or two with the sneaking notion that what the little fellow had said about folks and dogs might get him into heaven instead of keeping him out, but Seth wasn't going to hear from them! If they felt guilty, that wasn't going to help—probably, guilt was what was bringing ninety per cent of them to a boil! And if he was relying on those who thought the boy was dead, period, got hit by a ball, period—well, they weren't a drop in the bucket. Storm center. He used that word again. And he said that one of the most ominous warnings was that the children were not wriggling or squirming around. He reminded Seth that it was the Ku Klux Klan that still ran in the veins of those like Andy Boyd; that ever since Harry, ever since the Supreme Court decision, and now certainly since the recent row, they were just spoiling for the chance to show the niggers what was what around here. And that this opportunity presented itself, that they should be able to "show" them through meting it out first not to a nigger but to a nigger-lover—well, that was plainly more in the way of an opportunity than they could be expected to pass up!

He said, "They're *very* well represented in the auditorium this morning, Seth, in their tight-fittin' suits. They'd like nothing better than to defile a house of God in the name of God, Seth; yes, they would. Sort of extra. Christmas bonus. Lay down the law right. And they didn't need the sight of Jim, which they're right now taking in, to get their gorge up or their suits fittin' too tight. But I don't calculate the sight of Jim is calming them down any mite."

"No," Seth said woodenly (loving this man who was a

Peter, strong and warm and scared). "Why on earth did the ushers let Jim in?"

"We couldn't keep him out, Seth. What's the matter with you, son? How could we turn him away, when it's the custom—when it's done and been done for years? A white family's colored servants have the right to come to a white church to the funeral of somebody white they've been working for. You had a memory lapse? That's understood. We always save a pew, left back, for them."

"Jim wasn't Harry's servant," Seth said, but understanding he was being excessively stupid.

"No, he wasn't," Jesse said, with an edge about his voice. "He certainly was not! Seth?" Jesse took a step toward him. He had swallowed his voice and had to begin over. "Seth . . . *don't you really know who Jim is?*"

Seth looked at him, and in spite of the pressure of time, quite slowly, up and down. "I don't know as I follow what you mean."

"You know what his last name is, of course?"

"Of course," Seth said, on the defensive immediately. "His last name is Erwin, his mother's name, I believe. Slave-descended, if that's what you're driving at, from our slaves who took our name, so many of them. Yes, I know. And aren't there as many Tate Negroes as Erwin Negroes around here, Jess?"

"Yes, there are," Jesse said slowly and gently. "Jim is Sarah's son, Seth. And of course Sarah was already carrying around that last name of Erwin before she went to cooking for your folks long about—when was it?—nineteen-fifteen, sixteen, thereabouts—and how long did she stay on with you?—nine or ten years?"

They looked at each other. Jesse took out his handkerchief and gave his face another treatment. A memory came back to Seth. He was standing on the other side of the thorn hedge which separated him from the block of kitchen windows, made of that old wavy glass divided into prim, small panes. He saw his father, in wide-striped shirt and disappearing belt (a belt that appeared and disappeared in rolls of flesh) and open fly, on his way through the kitchen, giving Sarah a sharp smack to jelly-like buttocks which shook and shook in reply. *On his way through.* Sarah, with her mouth open, showing all her wealth of gleaming gold and ivory, and with a pan of biscuits held high; Sarah laughing fit to kill. That was all there was to the memory. If it recurred, he had no way of knowing whether the recurrence was in him or out there on the other side of the wavy glass.

"I'm not saying it's true," Jesse said in the same gentle way. "I'm merely reminding you of what got talked up when Harry . . . Sarah was black as Africa, Seth, and . . . *Jim's out there now!*"

Seth did not say anything.

"Jim and Jimbo too," Jesse murmured.

Seth said nothing. But it occurred to him to wonder—idly—whether the town was also as well informed on that which he and Carrie had never so much as once mentioned between them, let alone to anybody else. Oh, of course everybody knew of the frittered fortune, knew that literally all there was left of it for Carrie was that one Persian rug, now legend, since Carrie had accepted it without a whimper and sold it—some said for $300, some said for $700—and promptly started playing the stock market. With exactly what results was anybody's guess, because besides having

a secretive nature, Carrie liked to "talk poor," this "talking
poor" being probably the only voluptuous streak in her.
But that these results were not from the start very incon-
siderable was suggested by the way that fellow from Bache
& Co. began kowtowing to her and the veiled hints Jesse
Tate himself had occasionally let fall. Then—and this *was*
one of those open secrets—and this was wherein hung the
tale Seth had earlier dismissed with a grimace—about five
years ago, by a coup that left certain quarters breathless,
Carrie had actually, or virtually, got control of Royall Furniture Company, stockwise, which left poor Carl Lindemann,
its Yankee president, still staggering under the load of fear
and admiration for her that he carried. Some contended,
however, that Carrie's coup came as no surprise to Carl
Lindemann who, under the name of Comstock Associates,
the supposedly Yankee firm which had bought out Royall,
had been fronting for Carrie the entire time. However that
might be, he was officially mum about Carrie's control,
though his manner of treating her was so transparent that
he might much better shout. Oh yes, the whole thing was
kept an official secret, according to Carrie's specifications,
but everybody knew (with the one intriguingly possible
exception of the late Harry Hibbard, who had only worked
for Royall as a salesman, after all, until very close to the
end of his life) and with the added fillip of being forbidden
such knowledge. All of which pointed to why Carrie was
so venerated (and so feared) in the man's world of business. It was why she was granted that special niche, quite
independent of the usual woman leader's "civic" affairs
and garden-club-sewing-circle doings. But it also pointed
to why, if you wanted to see it that way, although Carrie

would prefer it if you didn't, she was so close to holding the town in her pocket. But did the town also know (because Carrie's mother and Seth's father had had the grace —and the means, thanks to Abel—to leave Peegram; to frequent such far-off spots as Sun Valley and Las Vegas, as Saratoga and Monte Carlo and Mexico City)—did they all know, then, that his father and Carrie's mother had lived their last jelly-years together in fornication? (And as one last stroke of collusion—after the fornication and after the heroin and after Flora's quack cures and after the "system" of beating the gaming tables and after the other "system" of picking the horses—dying within a week of each other.) Was their living together in sin also one of these open secrets but one that the town protected *them* (Carrie and him!) from? Probably. He had never known with sureness, never had it confirmed beyond doubting, who Jim was, until this moment. And it did put a curious new face on the past!

Jesse was saying, "Seth, we did call the police. We had to."

"You and who?" Seth asked. "You and Carrie?"

"That's right. And I'm sorry we had to go over your head—that's what I've been leading up to, and maybe we did make the wrong decision. I didn't feel any safer when they came in. But they aren't standing in the aisles or anything like that. Just sittin' inconspicuous, and with some one or two outside, making themselves politely scarce, but there all the same, for Andy Boyd and his crowd to get a load of. Carrie figured the toughs would come, you see, Seth, even if she didn't figure in Jim."

Seth smiled. For a forgetting second he felt almost triumphant. "And didn't figure in—or you either, it would seem—that Andy Boyd's kid brother is on the force—police force, I mean, Jess."

"Yeah," Jesse said, and might well have wiped the streaming sweat from his face again. "Yeah," he repeated. "You've got something there, I'm afraid. They do look mighty sleepy-eyed or made out of wood or something. I'm afraid they're not going to help—I admit that. Maybe make it worse. Like we were daring the toughs. Or just managed to get more of them—in uniform. That what you mean?"

"Perhaps. They'll obey us in the letter, of course. In spirit, they may belong to Andy Boyd."

"Yeah," Jesse said, sucking in his breath. "And too late to do anything about it now. . . . Pray, Seth. It's all we have left. God has *got* to help us; He must. Seth, pray if you ever have!"

(Had he ever? Seth wondered. And did he believe in anything "out there" that Jess had been so busily describing? In anything at all?)

Jesse said, "It's jam-packed, Seth. Sardines aren't packed closer. You couldn't get a piece of paper between them. Seth, make the service short. That was Carrie's final word, that's what she whispered in my ear to bring back here to you. Don't orate, whatever you do."

"I'm not in the habit of orating," Seth said stiffly. "I never do, unless the family insists."

"And don't even mention the boy."

"How about the bird?" Seth came back at him at once.

Jesse blinked. "And be careful—be *most* careful what you read out of the Book. You might not better even say, 'Suffer the little children to come unto me and forbid them not, for of such is the kingdom of heaven.' Get it over *quick,* Seth.

That's the idea, that's the only way. Then we'll have only the graveside to wrestle with and you can make that shorter than short. Get it all over before it has the chance to begin."

Jesse broke off. They listened, both of them, intently, to the rising organ swell of "Nearer My God to Thee."

"Well, it's time," Seth said. "That's something."

Jesse had his hand on the door knob, had it half turned.

"Seth?"

"Yes?"

"Your boy, William Morrison . . ."

"Yes?" Seth said, feeling his slow, cold rage swelling in him, and as if in competition with the mounting organ sound. (There must be something in training, regularly, the son to abominate the father, the father the son. It was—it must be—good old Erwin tradition and the secret of why the Erwins had survived this long.) "Yes?"

"I thought you might like to know where he's sitting."

"No," Seth said, "I don't care."

"Well, but . . . he came, sort of stamping in."

"With his mother, of course."

"Of course. But . . . Well, as you might say, he looked the situation over. And he didn't go on up to the family-reserved pews, though you could tell he saw them perfectly well, saw where Carrie and Fred and all your cousin-kin are sitting. He waved off Pete Avery—Pete was ushering him. Well, Seth, for everybody's being packed so close, there was one awfully vacant pew except for Roger Patton and Miss Lyerly. And William Morrison, sort of herding his mother, you know—she didn't have a thing to do with it—

looked all wilted and flabbergasted—well, sort of herding her, he sits himself down, big as you please, right next to Miss Lyerly, his mother on the other side. Nothing she could do. Thought you might want to know, Seth, just in case . . ." His voice failed him, "Nearer My God to Thee" drowning it out perhaps.

"You go ahead," Seth said, "you've got to go around. I'm coming."

Jesse went—ran.

Seth stood there for a moment, flexing his hands, a habit that seemed to be new with him. "All right, Harry," he muttered. "It's me, word against deed. All right, Harry, old friend."

3

"The Lord is my shepherd; I shall not want. He maketh me to lie down in green pastures: he leadeth me beside the still waters. He restoreth my soul:"

—Realizing it is quite possible for the hypnotist to be the one hypnotized in the end; the wrecker wrecked; the surgeon serving his own turn, anesthetized upon the table. He coasted —he had not made his entrance to handle a general lassitude, an interstitial, an intercellular boredom. He did not understand. (And he did not look in Martha Lyerly's direction, in his son's direction.) He would have understood to the marrow violent emotion screwed to the breaking point and was with all his life prepared to pit the voice-and-word against it in ultimate challenge; to try holding the contemplated deed at bay, thus. And it was Jesse who had set that stage for him;

set his dream of dreams on stage for him, this dream that had run under all the *etcetera* dreams of his youth and which had assumed such atomic proportions in recent years: the nation on the verge of destroying the world with atomic bombs and at this juncture himself rising to the floor of Congress and *talking* the nation out of it—*Repent ye, now, O Israel*—so eloquent that the nation thereafter forever desisted and monuments were erected to the one Seth Erwin who had reshaped the destiny of the world with voice-and-word his weapon. In this more particular Peegram staging—hazardous at best, because a man's dream cannot be put to the test of reality without a most ghastly unraveling—he would have soothed, caressed and worked the word magic and the word power, would have poured forth a liquid gold. (The voice was never in better form.)

"... *he leadeth me in the paths of righteousness for his name's sake.*"

And it was as if they *yawned.* He did not know what to make of it. Usually so adroit at taking the collective pulse that it was a trait he was ashamed of, he was now completely adrift. Could such somnolence be faked? It was not the storm-center sort Jess had described. Why did its import escape him?

"*Yea, though I walk through the valley of the shadow of death, I will fear no evil: for thou art with me; thy rod and thy staff they comfort me.*"

True, it was not his usual congregation, which he knew pew for pew and face for face in his entrails. But he had after all much experience of funeral congregations behind him; he had Harry's funeral behind him. Of no use, it would seem, because—with two categories of exceptions—he had never bored anybody in his life. He did not know what he was supposed to do. A congregation is laid out in hills and dales of heads (children are not tall); a ten o'clock light falls through stained-glass windows (these windows are without imagery, without agony) and what is he supposed to do? That it was no ordinary funeral he could have told (certainly) from the moment he missed the great waves of sentimentality bearing in and breaking over him. (Oh, but sentimentality is saving!) And from the absence of what he called "funeral thoughts" which ordinarily crested the big waves of POOR CARRIE OR WHOEVER—CARRIE OR WHOEVER IS SO BRAVE! with the little foam and spray of *Well, she didn't get a new dress, I see, I'm right glad I made that pie from scratch, the crust was worth it, if I say so myself it melts in the mouth, has she spotted my floral piece yet, I wonder, well, it's Waddell's best so I'm not going to worry about that, but that cross over there is sure tacky, two piddling lilies that you can't find for the fern, I declare, must be Lon Avery's, that boy is as close as the bark on a tree, and Bill Waddell told me himself he's always trying to squeeze a $6.60 look out of a $3.30 price, there's Alma, peaked as all get out, puts her in mind of poor Sam's passing, I've no doubt, and of course he didn't get as many flowers, Elaine's dress is new anyhow*—POOR WHO-EVER—WHOEVER IS SO BRAVE! (Eyes ceremoniously oozing; Kleenex fresh, handkerchiefs virgin.) And from the absence of the usually steady undertow, the mordant review or second seeing (in the mind's eye) beyond the blind black wall of the casket (high on trestles) and into its white satin belly where the dead lay rouged and distended with embalming fluid, lifelike, as they would assure themselves, while sniffing the scent of flowers, finger-thick around them, the perfumed envelope for rot they had provided, not placing their faith altogether in rouge and fluid or even the vault that carried the guarantee of ninety years.

All this was the poem he knew so well how to raise from doggerel to the sublime, but which did not apply today, for boredom! He had come to reshape violence and they offered him somnolence. They told him he bored them when he had never bored anybody, with those two categories of exceptions, the first category being Carrie who habitually slept through his sermons and services with her eyes politely open, and the second being children (he did not like children) whose faculty for converting Moses into General Mark Clark or Davy Crockett and continuing their own dreaming, fidgeting course undisturbed he had never pretended to be able to cope with. Well, the law was operating in reverse this morning, if *that* was ominous. These, the children and Carrie, were the ones not bored—Carrie behind her calm; the children attentive without any degree of disguise.

"Thou preparest a table before me in the presence of mine enemies: thou anointest my head with oil; my cup runneth over."

(He would not look at Martha Lyerly at all.)

His mind skittered like some hunted rabbit and came full on, against Carrie, for guidance. But (and as minds have the habit of doing) it immediately burrowed down through time, while still firmly here in the now, and announced formally to Carrie, I've forgot how much you did weigh when you were born. But you were so big you broke all the records around here and your dainty mother Flora was mortified beyond endurance, particularly as it was demonstrated beyond dispute you weren't a boy. Flora, lifting a wee finger—remem-

ber? you ought to remember, because I do; it got to be a
habit she kept up through the years—Flora lifting that finger
aloft and batting her blue eyes and saying, "But *surely* something is missing?" Remember? And did you understand,
petunia? Ah, she was crazy-wild about me; pulled my ears,
the lobes, whenever I came near. But she could pin no
ruffles on you! You were no girl to the dainty Flora, were
you? And you were not a complete boy and that was a terrible blow to Abel as well, who had bought Flora as sure as
his pappy ever bought a brood mare. He had to stop prais-
ing her points after you'd been around awhile and nothing
else was forthcoming; oh, he lived to rue the day he ever
departed from the Erwin type of wife. Flora with wee finger
erect. "Just one teeny itsy bitsy eensy mistake." Meaning
you, Carrie, without . . . *you* know. And it's still the
generally held view about you around here, don't think it
isn't, merely because people don't use words to give it expression, and that's why we're all so fascinated. And if Harry
alone did not hold this general view, if Harry alone found the
woman in you, think: Harry's dead, and as the poet says,
*The grave's a fine and private place but none, I think, do
there embrace.* Did you mourn because you could not mourn
him, Carrie? What curiosity your bedroom scene provoked—
oh, my dear, my lovely, you could have been *a joke!* Instead,
look at you, you're dangerous. . . . But do you remember
how Abel told you (taught you) it didn't matter what you
were like, how awkward or how oversized, because you were
who you were and life would not pass you up? And when the
time was ripe for young men to come calling and the young
men stayed away, the way Abel comforted you: you could
still take your pick, he said; he said Prince Charming would

not stand *you* up. And meantime, Sethie Boy was impressed into squiring you around. Darling, you were a dinosaur trained to do the two-step; you were a battleship with steel-plated and impervious sides, did I ever tell you? Didn't I spill out at least some small part of the red-hot shame that consumed me that night we had to lead the figure, you and I, at the Senior Ball? You see, I knew Abel would never send me off to college, would never leave me a brass farthing— dear girl, it became the condition—if I did not see to it you got your invitations; and no one, Carrie, but *no one* would invite you to the ball, not even as a favor to me, not even bribed, so that I had to make that entrance with you myself. Didn't you hear the cheers? Titter-cheers, they were. But then old Abel's prophecy did come true after all, didn't it? Because Harry Hero Hibbard could have had any girl in Erwin County. He *must* have chosen your hulk for the money (except insofar as he might not have; there is, I grant, the suspicion he did not; and, I grant, he never peeped when, as it turned out, the sum of your substance was one rug). So Harry came riding the white horse, and would you like to know how the wits described your marriage? They said you two were committing hari-kari, only they spelled it harry-carrie, of course, and without maybe suspecting there might be something in your natures rhyming deeper than your unfortunate names. . . . Oh, Carrie, Carrie girl, if you don't mourn Harry's death, I do. He might have saved us from you. He was anyway our only hope. He did take you on, man to woman, by God, and in the only way, I'm sure, God ever meant it to be played out. . . . You took that one rug, left to you in the spirit of mockery, and by way of that rug you did finally get your hooks into the great Royall Furni-

ture Company that our fornicating parents would have
deprived you of, didn't you? But should I congratulate you,
when it was this same Royall Furniture Company that, oh
so incidentally, your husband worked as a salesman for?
Did it afford you such pleasure? And you—you—thought up
those prayer rooms and such, for Royall, dropping your
thoughts into the receiving slot of my mind. (Had they
tried to make you Woman of the Year, you'd have politely
refused.) Oh, God. You were the one (don't deny it) who
got the wind up over Harry. You made me fire Martha
Lyerly. Oh, I know everybody was with you, me too—and
I know we were all with you against Harry—but how is
it *you* always contain everybody in your bowels? Don't you
know women don't make good history? "Emancipation,"
"equality," but I tell you that if we could even just rid ourselves of the deluge of women taking over our public
schools where they've virtually got the future's men in hock
for the twelve years of their shaping up, *we'd* make history
shine again. As you contain us, Carrie, as you embody us,
you are our strait jacket. For all your power you lack the
real power and the flexibility of the man, you do. And look
what we're coming to! Oh, Carrie, my dinosaur, my heart, I
can only wish that today you were the one resting in that
box. (And for one fractured second he listened, because
it seemed to him he heard the faintest, faintest whisper,
"Well, you fight her, Seth. You're left." His eyes smarting,
because it seemed to be Harry's dear, hated, forgotten
voice.) Carrie, I tell you, whatever happens here today, or
doesn't happen, it's your fault. Even the child in the casket
is your "fault." This is your show. Take it, Carrie. I'm tired
of fronting for you. Take it, Carrie; I'm through. The reply,

the same as before, very simple, coming back to him from the calm, unblinking eyes: Make it short.

"Surely goodness and mercy shall follow me all the days of my life: and I will dwell in the house of the Lord for ever."

He did not pause. He had the place marked in the big pulpit Bible and he turned to it straight off. But in the act of doing so, he shifted his eyes from Carrie's face to Fred's face, Fred sitting hard on by Carrie, Fred the oldest son, and only brother of the child they buried today, and Fred looking enough like the young Harry to be the young Harry himself, so that he would no doubt have encountered, these nine months, oblique looks in such number as to make him maybe want to undergo plastic surgery, for all his supple body and handsome face. Fred was a firmly fleshed ghost, in the snares of adolescence, whose chemistry of suffering was without the explosion of pimples; yes, Fred was bored.

"O Lord our Lord, how excellent is thy name in all the earth! who hast set thy glory above the heavens."

And in the sleepy swim of faces, and as if against his better will and judgment, he now picked out Jim's, sure enough left back, as Jesse had assured him it would be (right back from his own perspective) but with Jimbo's face, if it was alongside, out of his ken. One could make little dents, as in putty, in a face like that, like Jim's. It was not slender, it was not delicate, had none of the beauty accorded by tradition to the child of love or the child of mixed races. This while it was certainly light enough, white enough to be called gray upon occasion—upon this occasion—something jogged him. Sufficiently different from his own face to be the face of his father that was before him. *And* it was

perhaps explainable why neither he nor Carrie would ever
forfeit respectability for any reason whatsoever, nor ever
leave Peegram, the only spot under heaven where their argument mattered. If they had a mutual prayer, it was that
there be room in Peegram for them both.

"*Out of the mouth of babes and sucklings hast thou
ordained strength because of thine enemies, that thou
mightest still the enemy and the avenger.*"

You could easily have skipped that, Jesse's face said.
For he had found Jesse's face, breached like a moon in
blackest sky; he had found Jesse mounting guard alone, and
without the company of any policeman, over the vestibule.
Again something jogged him; cried out, as it were, for his
attention.

"*When I consider thy heavens, the work of thy fingers, the
moon and the stars, which thou hast ordained; What is man,
that thou art mindful of him? and the son of man, that thou
visitest him?*"

His eyes swept the congregation more seeingly, returned
briefly to the family-reserved pews in front, to his "cousin-
kin," the intricacies and degrees of whose relation to himself he could not for his life have disentangled. And probably
no one else could, now that Aunt Phoebe and Aunt Deb
were no longer of this world, they being the only ones he
knew who were capable of moving through the whole mass
of names and relationships and coming up serenely with
Alicia, the seventh cousin of the second Zebulon's third
wife. Time was, nor was it so long ago, when anybody was
apt to be cousin to practically everybody within a radius
of thirty miles. He thought, the South's incest nightmare,
which can and does still scream for the color line, so com-

plex and now unknown and unmeasurable is the blood guilt. The last time "the connection," "the cousin-kin," had all turned out was for Harry's funeral. It was the last time he had seen them *en masse* and he recalled this as his own orientation became less somnolent—he ticked it off. . . . The next thing he ticked off, the next feature to claim (finally) his attention was this: in the low tide and general lassitude, there were, here and there throughout the auditorium, jutting up like posts out of the calm receding waters, certain figures whose lassitude, while evident, did not manage to extend itself into posture; their boredom was a non-postural phenomenon, as if finding its limit in yielding flesh confronted with unyielding steel. They were not so much bulging under their coats as bolt-up. These were not the policemen, to be sure, but Andy Boyd's henchmen whose interfered-with natural slouches might even be a minor miscalculation. Distributed in rather elaborate, rather geometric pattern (commanding the aisles and strategic positions), they stuck out like so many sore thumbs. It would have taken the blind not to see them! Andy Boyd himself was sitting toward the back, in an end seat on an outside aisle, under a window, and the only window in the place, he noted, that was open, as if incidentally, about a foot. Martha Lyerly (because he looked now; he had to) was sitting in front of Andy Boyd, Jim behind. The distance between Andy Boyd and vestibule-exit was not great; Jim was between him and it and *it* was guarded by Jesse, solus. The distance between Andy Boyd and the shining billiard-ball head of Roger Patton, flanking the Lyerly on one side (and what more than this head shining so luminously in the tender light could a hunter ask, to get his bearings by?)

—this distance was not great either, a matter of five rows, and the angle good. Andrew Boyd had the reputation of being a fine shot; it was not therefore unlikely that A. Boyd had taken the shooting honors upon himself. He was known to be somewhat piggish and a braggart who bragged best when he had something to brag about. Get out of the way, Jess. When that same fellow who betrayed his Lord three times before the cock crew got brave, he was crucified upside down.

"For thou hast made him a little lower than the angels, and hast crowned him with glory and honour."

But the window puzzled him: if a man was to vault out of it, shouldn't it be raised higher in readiness? No, he could see that a man could not even squeeze out, but a man might just claim that another man (any man would do; who knew what man?) had stood outside it and fired in (the angle would be right), and a man could conceivably, in one split second, drop his smoking gun out the foot-high crack and into the shrubbery below where, when it was discovered, it could pass as the nameless assassin's own that the nameless assassin had dropped before he ran. And how convenient, that Peegram Hardware could be allowed to stand ready to muddle or mislay the bill of sale on that same gun, and the police their records if there were such. He seemed to under-stand: one shot, electrically timed—Jim might not be killed—two shots might be considered to be too risky, after all—and Jim had not been figured in on this—though they would certainly not be made unhappy to find Jim on hand to wit-ness "the lesson"—and if Jim was not to be killed, Jess might not be hurt either, for the reason that Andy Boyd, having parted company with his gun, might not find it necessary to

his dignity to break for freedom; might indeed stand about,
at his ease, in the herd. One shot? Two? As for these others
of the disturbed posture, it could be that they had brought
their toys along in the spirit of companionableness, and just
in case their Andy met opposition from some unexpected
emergency quarter—not, necessarily, that they planned to
use them.

*"Thou madest him to have dominion over the works of thy
hands; thou hast put all things under his feet:"*
—The general lassitude, the general sleep. (His throat a
little dry now, his voice a little the worse for that, and he
must keep the hurry out of it now. He should not have
embarked on the eighth psalm; not having fully made up
his mind whether to include it or not, he had made his decision in defiance of the calm command of Carrie's eyes.)
The lassitude. Perhaps its import was coming home to him
too! It was a vast permissive innocence; a renunciation; an
abdication from responsibility; an inaction offered in the
teeth of action which was not theirs by definition and had
never been theirs; the complete innocence of complicity; a
forgetting that was *a priori;* they had gone home when they
came in. Oh, yes, the deed was done already, this deed
they would spare him—and themselves—from, and they were
merely waiting out *subsequent* formalities. I'll be damned
if that's so, he thought. It has *not* happened yet! He swallowed for the sake of lubricating spit in the throat. Wasn't
it odd that when he could not, for instance, find Jimbo's
head at all, William Morrison should deem it necessary to
sit so tall? Almost as tall as the Lyerly herself and much too
near. His eyes slid over Elaine—*she* was plenty far. Was
Andy Boyd such a famous shot then? Only one better in

these parts—Harry Hibbard—who was hardly in the running.
His eyes hastened over Andy Boyd's red package of a face:
it remained unsoftened in the roseate light and had not, like
others around it, succumbed to any pastel tints of pink. It
was a raw beefsteak of a face, inviolate. He seemed to sense
there would be some very obvious signal, one somehow more
understood than prearranged, one not involving of course
any previous verbal exchange between *the doers* and *the
sleepers*. What? What could it be? He would surely unwit-
tingly give it (but what?) and the ones who were reared up
like posts would go down like posts hewn, and the rest, by
slumping down a little lower than they were slumped now—
a mere extension of lassitude; they were half out of the way
already—would be safely out of range, all except the Lyerly
and, for that matter, Roger Patton and Jim, should he be
turned on, and Carrie too, though she was so far front as
to be altogether out of danger, and the children whose lack
of height, with the exception of his son, was their protection, these who were the exceptions to the general drift,
whose very attention or fear, curiously enough, rendered
them posturally available. The Lyerly (and Jim) being
exactly the ones too primed and too ready to do other than sit
up straighter than ever should the signal by some chance get
itself communicated to them, but they were also of course
exactly the ones (with himself thrown in?) who would miss
the signal entirely, whatever that signal was (*thou hast put
all things under his feet:*).

"*All sheep and oxen, yea, and the beasts of the field; The
fowl of the air, and the fish of the sea, and whatsoever pass-
eth through the paths of the seas.*"

It annoyed him that the children, even yet, even now,

should be taking their bearings by the Lyerly. What did they think she was—a lighthouse? Why did they have to keep cutting their eyes toward her at this juncture? Could not their attentiveness have worn off? Could they not be looking *the other way?* At the casket, at least? Jim kept his eyes trained on her too. And she—oh, hopeless—was not unafraid of her fear. And he thought—simply wondering— should he say good-by? Wave to her? Her contempt for him was sweet; it shone out, as she sat there being a lighthouse. It will be quick, he promised her, it will only blow your head off. It's the children we mourn for. My head blown off *in church?* she asked him. You never should have come to church, he told her. . . . A shocking mouth, she had. A shockingly beautiful woman. He could not help that! Bony and spectacled, she might have had her chance. But no, she had to have vital breasts and vital thighs, and that almost-secret carelessness about grooming which a man noted because it meant giving. That's what the mouth meant. And was she the kind to stand champion for a cause? God forbid. She was the kind you undressed in your mind. Not the whore-kind, to be sure, but the even more devastating kind that spells passion and unlimited yielding tenderness combined (and to each one!). Doomed. It was not fitting, not decent, to translate a social problem thus; to see the radical and the enemy naked in one's arms. She *should* pay for that with her life. Because if the men went after her out of shame for the secret thoughts she provoked in them, the women followed in yet louder cry, for what they sensed in their men; the women hating her most for that and for her coloring, more than for the corrupting of their children, which was bad enough. What man in here (unless the Man of God,

as one could devoutly wish) wouldn't fall for the chance to
settle the problem in bed, to silence her forever there in love
(and it could be done), but that failing, and in daylight it
failed very much, death was their permission, second best.
The dead might bury their dead today. She was sexy in the
deepest sense. In the present contingency, with all its overtones, there was not a greater affront.

*"O Lord our Lord, how excellent is thy name in all the
earth!"*

He was through now, except for one brief postscript that
he need not turn to any new place in the pulpit Bible in
order to deliver; he knew it off by rote. He leaned a little
toward them, as if seeking to annihilate pulpit and rostrum,
and his eyes (for the first time) skimmed the casket.

He said, *"Are not two sparrows sold for a farthing? And
one of them shall not fall on the ground without your
Father. But the very hairs of your head are all numbered.
Fear ye not, therefore, ye are of more value than many
sparrows."*

He was moved; his voice broke. Then, as he was in the
act of bowing his head to lead them in closing prayer, he
saw it. (Of course. *Prayer.* When all heads go down—except
an atheist's—when all eyes are closed, even policemen's, and
most properly so, when it comes to giving evidence afterward in a court of law. Very neat, withal.) He saw Andy
Boyd make the sudden electric movement that brought him
to his feet and into the aisle, saw his left hand at the coat
buttons, the right hand diving in. In his church, he had
never used the Brother-Sister form of address. But in the
instant his voice whipped out.

"Yes, Brother Boyd," he cried. "Yes, our brother in the

Lord! We wait on you now. Will you not be the one to lead us in a word of closing prayer?"

The hand with the buttons fumbled drastically. Not an adult head turned.

"Lead us, Brother!"

The man's face worked.

"Lead us all and let us all together pray to the Lord!"

Seth made the sign to Gertrude, the organist; he threw a look at Jesse—the pallbearers must be in readiness; the funeral parlor assistants were already alert of course.

Brother Boyd's red package of a face was purple.

"Oh, God—" came an outlandishly crude, heavy, half-blaspheming, half-supplicating voice. "Uh . . . " And stopped altogether.

Seth picked him up immediately, though the prayer he had prepared in his mind had flown. He said, *"May the words of our mouths and the meditations of our hearts be acceptable in thy sight, O Jehovah*—oh, God. Amen."

For a second, the hush seemed destroying. But the music of "Abide with Me" came up strong (Gertrude was ever prompt). Seth stepped back from the pulpit. The pallbearers lurched forward, the funeral parlor assistants (it need hardly be said) were already in unctuous action (over the flowers). The congregation stood, as it was supposed to, in reverence. The casket must go out first.

4

On his way out of the church, Seth had managed to convey a hastily whispered message to Jesse. "Tell Jim *I said* not to

come to the graveside. Tell Roger Patton the same. Tell him
I said not to bring Miss L out there." (Assuring himself he
used the children's diminutive for her because it was
shorter.)

Seth had had enough experience with funerals always to
insist upon taking his own car out to the cemetery rather
than riding in one of the funeral-parlor limousines. That
way, even allowing for the amenities, he got away sooner.
Also, he had become adept at parking, with an eye to getting
out ahead of the crowd.

Peegram was proud of its cemetery and it was one of
those that are much "kept up": the graves as tidy as pin-
cushions, the grass a scrupulous green and definitely forewarned. The jealous, cantankerous old caretaker was apt
to call you up and tell you it had been such-and-such number of months since you had last visited your family's graves
with flowers. To him, the dead were alive and as jealous and
cantankerous as he. He had a most intimate speaking acquaintance with Peegram families but only as they were
turned under. His mind was such a garden of epitaphs that
that was the way he talked, in epitaphs. The Peegram
cemetery was somewhat hilly and there was a neat gravel
road winding around among the graves and ending where
it began—at the gates. Seth knew this road so well he could
almost have driven it with his eyes closed.

Some day, he decided, he was going to write the defini-
tive piece on Christians and vaults. It would have tremendous philosophical import; it would be suggested that the
whole fate of the impoverished earth was in the balance.
It would be subtly pointed out that the more zealous the
Christian the more was he apt to pay out for the vault, and

the more he paid out, the longer was the vault guaranteed
to keep the worms out of work. (With many sects, at the
graveside service now, it was no longer considered even *de
rigueur* to say "dust to dust.") He would write, "They *will
not* replenish the earth, they *will not* return to the earth,
they *will not* have immortality, at all, at all." And inasmuch
as Christians were conquering the earth, the big question
would be, how fast could the poor old earth get at Christian
cemeteries?

The service was finished before it began, the clod of red
earth smartly splatting the casket's side, a wind coming up
and flapping the canopy where a foolish sparrow was
perched peering down at them. Harry's grave, which was
the one alongside, was still patchy raw, the headstone not
yet settled. Since Jim and Jimbo had not come, the proportion of their importance seemed to fall off. But Roger and
Martha Lyerly were very much in evidence, whether in
defiance of his command or because Jesse had been unable
to get the word to them.

"We commend this body . . ."

It was all foreshortened, all over. Out of the corner of
his eye he had observed where Andy Boyd had parked his
1955 four-door Dodge—directly behind Roger Patton's old
vintage Ford.

The sky was exceedingly blue, the clouds nestling and
playful, cavorting like lambs. William Morrison stood broadside to everything, and as if perversely, since he stood so
stolid, nevertheless seeing the sparrow looking over these
humans out of its bead of an eye.

Seth thought he would let the handshaking and the well-
modulated greetings and the well-chosen clichés of comfort

go today. He stepped up quickly to Roger Patton and Martha
Lyerly and his son (broadside, in front of her). Looking over
his son's head (height, now, an advantage), he said, "I will
drive Miss Lyerly home, Roger, if you please." And without
waiting for an answer, he took her under the elbow. "Come
on," he said. That she came meekly should have surprised
him, he supposed, but did not.

He had her in the car. On the way around to his own side,
he noted that William Morrison did not turn toward Elaine
and Carrie and Fred, with whom he must surely have ridden
out, but went walking off alone, his hands bulging fists in
his pockets—a small, solitary, dogged figure who would probably walk all the way back to town by the side of the highway, Seth thought angrily, turning down all rides offered
him.

Seth maneuvered his car smoothly onto the gravel road, as
he did so seeing in his rear-view mirror that while certain
ones were piling hastily into the 1955 Dodge, it had not
yet budged. At the gates, he turned west, away from town.
This turn the swell of the hill behind would have shielded
from the sight of those in the Dodge. And they were in luck
in that the cantankerous old caretaker himself was back
there, being proprietary over the new grave—the ones in the
Dodge could ask him no questions and he could tell them
no truths. His foot moved steadily and smoothly down on
the accelerator. A curve in the highway abolished (in rear-
view vision) the gates of the cemetery now. Half a mile
further, he turned off the highway into what was known as
the Old River Road, narrow and rutted. He braked the car—
brought it to a crawl.

"When I'm so untouchable," she said, "I suppose I should congratulate you on your courage."

It was a beautiful road, despite the ruts and the potholes and the narrowness (all to be changed soon enough, since this was destined to become a "development," thanks to Carrie, and laid out in city lots, and with the road widened and paved). Overhead, the trees almost touched, forming a leafy arch. There were appearing and disappearing vistas of the river, still high and swollen this time of year. Little dogwoods in tender leaf and shining dark-leafed rhododendron bushes were everywhere tucked away amongst the pines and the oaks and the maples and, on the river side, willows as well, and reeds, and wild rough clumps of grass.

"Like it?" he asked.

"It's lovely," she admitted.

"Later, in the summer, there's such a tangle of honey-suckle and wild sweetpea vines and morning glories and I don't know what-all that you could use a machete to cut your way through."

Then, as if heading for a destination predestined, he pulled off the road and they bounced over a weed-choked path to what had once been known as "Harry's landing," now in a sad state of disrepair, but the river was very much before them. Behind them, on a rise, was what had once been Harry Hibbard's cabin, built with his own two hands, with love. Seth shut off the ignition and sat back.

"I've never seen the river till now," she said. "That's obvious."

She was looking out over the water—so bright in the sunlight that she half closed her eyes. The hazy blue line of the mountains was almost lost in the hazy blue distance. The little white clouds were much closer.

"I come out here sometimes," he said. (Nine months, the birth of second death—he pushed that thought from his mind.)

She had turned toward him and was looking him over. Next he knew, she would fix him with those great dark melting eyes and demand, "Do you believe in God?" He nearly laughed out. She wanted to quarrel, to have it out, to get at the root of the problem. Whereas he . . . did not believe he would tell her he had been busy saving her life, this bright and particular Saturday—was, in point of fact, formally engaged in that occupation at this minute. He thought it would please him to withhold that information from her. On a rise (which he could see in his rear-view mirror) stood a lone, rotting cabin, and they had just left the graveside of a child whose three-letter name was longer than the service said for him, and plying the highway was a 1955 Dodge with a man behind the wheel who had just said the first prayer of his career and was out seeking restitution; and thus, if a car standing stone still, with the ignition shut off, surrounded by weeds half as high as its fenders, was not to be construed as a car out of control, it was necessary they behave as though this were any other Saturday, taking no prizes, hardly worth an honorable mention, didn't she see? When bloody bubbles are forming on our lips, it is best to say, "Don't take no wooden nickels." It is always very moving. When all else is held in rear-view vision, and two are contained not in a casket but something else that measures, you swear, no larger; when you feel yourself snatched out from under, and you are aware your body is

a tight fit, and you do not approve of the way you're breathing—what's there to do, what else is there to do except keep
the mood light? So he watched while she fumbled with
cigarettes and matches. And he reached for the matches—
took them out of her hand—lighted the cigarette—pocketed
the matches. He should have called time out, in order to
congratulate himself.

"*Brother* Erwin," she said, her contempt for him shining
out. "Is it because you're such an aristocrat that you stooped
to that? . . . Seth the son of Zebulon the son of Seth, *clear
back?*" (This last she murmured.)

"Oh, *clear* back," he said. " 'Which was the son of Enos,
which was the son of Seth, which was the son of Adam,
which was the son of God.' I give you the Holy Writ."

"Thanks."

But he had scored: she smiled.

"Now, tell me," he said, "how is it you are a teacher?"

She—not he—was the one who laughed out, her laughter
filling the car, mixed up with a whole gale of cigarette smoke
and sunshine, which (he could see) she soaked up. The car
had never seemed so small. And the glare on the water
made it so that they had to sit turned toward each other,
full-face. And then, as he was discovering, she was nearly
as hard on his eyes as the water was.

She said, "Do you know I had it on the tip of my tongue
to ask you—how is it *you* are a preacher?"

Of course. He had known it all along. "I asked you first,"
he said. And to keep her occupied, "You aren't the type.
How will you stand the gaff? How did you ever plow through
an education degree? You do seem—intelligent."

"I am intelligent."

It was the gayest admission he had ever heard. He asked
for lightness and she gave him this unbearable gaiety. She
kept blowing smoke in his face, without waving it away; he
did not wave it away either.

He thought lovers were dreadful—excessive, like overripe
fruit. As a boy he had never had the experience of falling
head over heels in love, so that it had never properly occurred to him that it was possible for him to forget himself
in somebody else. He had rather supposed it was something
of which he was incapable. He was too suave, too self-
contained, too enamored of the convolutions of his own
being for any such letting down of the gates as was involved
in love. There was a lot of Paul in him: "I take pleasure in
my weaknesses, injuries and needs, in my persecutions and
distresses . . ." As they were his, his own, alone, with the
aloneness of all his years to vouch for the validity. She
didn't so much dazzle him as make him feel ill.

Was he to offer himself—his small, personal naïveté—as
distinct from all his learning, the Hebrew and Aramaic and
the Greek and the Latin and the German and the French;
all the theology and all the history and the literature and
the poetry and the music and the paintings that hung in the
gallery of his mind and that he had assembled there with
such care, the ones by El Greco and Rouault, Botticelli and
Michelangelo and Rembrandt, Cézanne and Delacroix and
Giotto and Piero della Francesca too? Was he to expose
himself, as distinct from the "sacred" reading and the "pro-
fane" footnotes, as distinct from irony and hypocrisy and
chapter and verse of the blameless life? Just a few scattered
memories and some threadbare fantasies and some dirty
thoughts? (It was his pleasure, at times, to address himself

in lewd and obscene language, silent torrents of it.) The
rebel without dandruff, the Man of the Year. He could have
wept. He could have taken (again) the whip to the pure
white marble of his loins. It happened to Paul, after all, on
an open road and in what was likely an epileptic fit. It was
over, all over with him and she would tell him of her happy
childhood! All the pleasure-and-pain would dredge the
bottom for his remains. All the pleasure-and-pain of firing
her came back; he could have known it then; *then* it was as
if he had dreamed her up out of a rib. Or maybe the first
time he had seen her, it had been the same. Why not face
it? Hadn't he run to the arms of irony, as to the arms of his
best friend, for consolation and protection? *Him* falling in
love with *her*? With still another shape and form of his
own ruin—but uncontrollable ruin, this time; the very sort
for which the preacher is run out of town—why not run her
out first? (Carrie's idea in the receiving slot of his mind.)
But then, all that filthy talk about her going the rounds and
gathering momentum; he knew she was hurt, turning in
her beauty like some hideous deformity, unable to hold her
head high and trade look for look. The cold depths of his
tenderness going warm: he told himself he wished, at least,
to give her back her beauty before she left. He did not like
to see any human being hurt like this, he told himself, only
today, only at this minute, understanding that his wish was
amply realized, because . . . she was young again and
whole and gay and tremulous and expectant and all that
God ever meant her to be, because . . . it was his power
(as he had so fought knowing) to make her so, to heal her
quicker than Jesus of Nazareth had ever healed an issue of
blood. He looked at her.

"It wasn't a bit easy," she was saying, still smiling at him.

He smiled. "What wasn't easy?" He took the matches out of his pocket, turning them over in his hand, studying them.

Softly: "Do you want me to start over?"

Softly: "I do." He did. He wanted not to miss anything. Not any cadence and not any word.

"Well," she said, "you asked me how I had got through an education degree and I was confessing it wasn't easy."

"Yes," he said, "I see."

"My father's an engineer, I mean the kind who operates a train. In the first grade—in those days first graders were graded—when I came home with my first report card which had, up and down, all As, you might say that coinciding with the moment my father saw it, my fate was sealed. After that, I didn't have a chance. *He* decided I was going to be a teacher. He has an uncommon regard for books and learning and he has the greatest respect for teachers—a profound and touching respect, almost religious."

"And where does *he* come from?"

"From Austria. He came over here when he was eleven."

"All right, then. But that's a downright un-American attitude for him to hold."

"Isn't it? And it was tough on me. Especially after my mother died—I was thirteen. He used to read aloud, all kinds of books, to her. But after her death, I was given the full battery—I can't tell you, even Newton's *Principia*. It was understood I was going to college. We made a little ceremony of putting away, in a tin box, the bond he would buy, each month, to pay for it. Then he found out that in this state one needs a Master's degree to get an A certificate. So I was to have that too. Right away. Before he should have to die, or retire, or something. He has funny notions about providing for us children. Not the least bit interested in leaving us property or money or anything like that—just training and skills, what we need to stand on our own and that's all. He's got his burying money set aside in the tin box but I don't think he carries a penny of insurance."

Seth nodded; they might be walking through a meadow together, picking buttercups and making "butter" on each other's hands. He recalled (oddly, he thought) the time in the bathroom of the stained-glass window that he had given Aunt Phoebe's and Aunt Deb's old claw-foot tub a pedicure with the bright-red nail polish stolen from Flora. So far as he knew, nobody had ever noticed the stunning effect. He would tell Martha Lyerly about it.

"So I had to stomach the education courses," she said. "There wasn't any other way. But since my father had already 'educated' me, reading me all those books and putting the habit of study into me, I endured—I even made the little cut-outs, as required, and pasted up pictures in scrapbooks, as 'projects.' When I walked across the platform for my M.A., my father was there. In awe of me, you know. I . . . well, I've never had the heart to tell him the topic they made me do my thesis on. From a great distance, after the ceremonies were all over, he handed me an envelope. In it there was a ticket to Southampton and money for a year's stay in Europe. (My brothers and sister had contributed too.) It was his cherished idea that I should see from where I had sprung before settling down to a career. I spent a lot of my time in Salzburg. Peegram is my first job."

"You came from Salzburg to *Peegram*?"

Her lips trembled a little. "You could say that."

"And he's still living, your father?"

"Yes."

"And as proud of you as ever, I suppose?"

She hesitated. "Yes."

He was angry. "Then why in heaven's name—why, at least, didn't you go into college teaching where there is still, even in this country, some little prestige and honor attached?"

"College teaching isn't for me. I did have to consider *me*. For me, kids."

"Why?"

"I don't know exactly. College teachers are an elite dealing with an elite. They aren't in on the ground floor. They're in a different world from the real world. I see no reason why a lower-school teacher shouldn't be intelligent and like books, do you?"

"No, except they are not intelligent and do not like books— that's been proved by all sorts of embarrassing studies. It's the guaranteed way to avoid books while getting through college—you've just admitted that. They're a stupid and inferior breed to begin with—the universities and colleges which are turning them out are admitting that. Then the system further destroys them—they're overworked and harassed; they dry up and wither away. Is it your idea you'll escape the withering? How old are you?"

"Twenty-five," she said demurely, yielding to the luxurious and headlong onslaught of his anger. (How sweet it was. When he was forty-one.) Looking up demurely into his eyes. Demurely asking, "And have there been any studies made showing what sort, in the way of talent and native ability, go into preaching?"

"It doesn't make any difference," he told her. "They are

called by God. God speaks through them. They're his vessels."

"I see."

They looked away from each other. He could feel their mood changing. Desperately, he affected casualness. "Have a job yet for next year?"

"No, not yet. But there's hardly been time." Adding, "Roger says I won't get one in this state. We'll see."

He fingered the matches. They watched the water, the unbelievable, unbearable shimmer of it. He became aware of the sound of its running.

"Why did you do it?" she asked in a low voice, without turning toward him. "What kind of game have you been playing? You went out of your way to bring it to people's attention that I didn't go to church, when all the while you couldn't have cared less, and maybe you even admired me for staying away. You get me fired from my job for my stand on segregation when that stand—I don't care what all these church-going Christians say about it—is, incidentally, the only possible stand a thinking Christian can take. How could you? I'll never forgive you for it."

Tenderly, he picked the cigarettes out of her lap, selected one and placed it between her beautiful lips; then lighted it for her with the matches he had made his.

"There," he said, "there."

"Why? You *shall* answer me."

"You're just not small-town material."

"That's one way of putting it."

"I do what I can."

"You'd do a lot more—and it would have gone a lot differently—if you had defended me."

He said, "Even Roger couldn't defend you on your own grounds."

"Roger!" She turned toward him then, fast enough. "Roger. But Roger does not believe as I do, so why should he defend me? You do!"

"How do you know?"

"I know." (She was crying.)

He said gently, "If I had defended you, on your own grounds, I should not be able to stay on in Peegram any more than you can. Don't you see?"

"So? So what? Is Peegram the world? As a minister, have you no sense of duty, to be honest, regardless? Oh, you *have* tampered with yourself."

(Ah, so young.) "In the first place," he said, "I am committed to staying."

"*Why?* I don't understand that either. 'You can't go home again.' If there's a thing I know, it's that you don't belong here."

He looked at her—strangely. " 'Seth the son of Zebulon,' " he murmured. "Martha." (Having never said her name.) "The Egyptian sun-god was Sutekh, or Set, who appears in Genesis as Seth the son of Adam. Well, the Egyptians worshiped Set in the likeness of an onager or wild ass. Do you follow me at all?"

But she said (she had of course not known his father, never had she laid eyes upon Zebulon), "I have the feeling that if you preachers did take the segregation issue into the pulpit—if you did, Sunday after Sunday, plug for integration—why, with the church as strong as it is in the South, desegregation couldn't lose. This is something preachers could really do!"

He had to laugh. "And why do you suppose, my dear, the church *is* so strong in the South? The first preacher around here who tried to do as you suggest—oh, I don't mean 'taking a stand,' some of them have done that and then politely pigeonholed the matter forever; so have some of the churches; why, the Southern Baptist Convention adopted a resolution last June in St. Louis; but the first preacher who really took desegregation into the pulpit and, as you say, plugged for it Sunday after Sunday as the only possible position for the Christian—well, he could go peddle his papers! There are a few exceptions, like the Catholics. But what are the Catholics around here? Already, in Madison, not a preacher but a highly trained professional church worker has been told to get out because he made it known that he was in sympathy with the NAACP. The particular church fired him, stating plain-out that that was the reason; this while their church synod has taken a stand favoring integration. It can't be done. There are these certain ironclad prejudices you can't run counter to. Don't you think *you* might be getting to know that?"

"You won't mind that what I think is you're a hypocrite and a coward, will you?"

He did mind. He minded so much that he took the whip he had reserved for himself to her and brought it down with all his strength. *"You love and respect your father."*

"Yes!" She was terribly startled.

"I don't love and respect mine—I never did—I don't think, ever. (Calmer.) And I've got a notion it makes all the difference in the world. You've been given the passport, I haven't. Nor do I suppose it's possible to lead an altogether meaningless life. I think I've done very well, not to be a murderer or a felon or a pervert or a screaming maniac."

He looked down at his hands so rigidly gripping the steering wheel—bent all his ferocity upon them. Relax! he ordered and watched them let go the wheel and fall lifeless at his sides. He dared them to try that rapid, peculiar flexing motion; they did not.

He wanted to say, "You belong to one of the crazy, foolish, priestly vocations too." He wanted to quote poetry. He wanted to put his head down on the wheel and close his eyes and feel everything begin to drain slowly out of him. All his life he had waited to be accused. Hypocrite. Coward. Accusation would mean the consummation. Only this morning, in his study, hadn't he noted, as the last crowning touch to his despair, that his shudder was a solitary one? The time came and he lashed out, he sniveled. He stared at the water and the sky and the distant mountains and the flirtatious clouds; at the tall, rank weeds that seemed already to have claimed the car, already bending to envelop the intruder in their midst. *"Do you believe in God?"* That had to come still. He: "Do you *believe* in weeds? Does it matter a particle whether you do or don't? Belief is simply another manifestation of conceit, vanity." He—the arch snob—in quivering, intestinal sincerity—continuing: "I was interested in how the great spiritual laws apply to *the many*. And, as these laws are explored (we've only just started), how *the many* might reap the benefits. Art is for the very few, we don't get around that. . . . Consider: wherever Christianity has been overthrown, worse has been substituted. And Christianity's hold on the popular imagination is immense—it is the religion of the Son. Christianity cannot be overthrown, therefore Christianity will have to be changed from within, denial and self-sacrifice injected with great doses of their opposites. I used to think these massive repressions we have built Christianity upon had to be dealt with from within. I craved to be involved in modern man's rediscovery of God. In the church, too, because, with reference to *the many*, it seemed quite clear to me that, like it or not, it was the church which was going to be one of the main instruments."

He shifted about, setting his back to the door, getting as far away from her as possible. Even in his thoughts, all his hopes and aspirations were carefully placed in the past tense.

"What makes you think death is any less cruel than life is?" he asked her abruptly. "Suppose the resurrection was an historical fact. Have you ever thought of that? Not to be allowed to die as a part of the tragic proposition? Remember, in *Crime and Punishment*, when Raskolnikov utters that cry, 'Only to live, to live and live!' Mine is, 'Only to die.'"

Danger. Her dark, melting eyes searching his. He knew it was necessary that their quarrel hang suspended between them, because there was no terminating it except in a disaster greater by a thousand times than the quarrel itself. It was the quarrel that would have to save them.

"Yes," she said slowly, "death is very much on our minds today."

"You demand an explanation from me. I don't have one to give you. Maybe I used to have some ideas. Now I could only lie. Something has happened here, mixed up with people and forces you couldn't possibly grasp, not being 'of us.' I'm everything you said I was. At least, I can know when I'm through, and from now on, confine all my efforts to being graceful. Does it please you to hear me 'confess'?"

She didn't look away, she kept right on searching his eyes.

The entire landscape was nothing but eyes. Mine are green and hers are brown.

"I'm not at all sure Ray's death was the tragedy I thought it was," she said.

He hated her.

"He was so much like you," she said. "He would have grown up to be like you. I think one of you is enough, Seth Erwin."

And you, dead and unable to speculate upon death, with the sun shining on without you right now; tomorrow, an undertaker's work of art, embalmed, with or without a head. You, in my debt. Do I or don't I tell you? That I, in full dress and regalia, all hypocrisy and all cowardice, was the one—one of me was enough—to stop Andy Boyd from pulling a trigger.

But—and undoubtedly this was appropriate—it was the image of Andy Boyd who stopped Seth now. His right hand had gone out and was within inches of her neck; a matter of seconds, and the hand would have cupped itself around the neck and he would have jerked her violently toward him, and the first kiss would have been violent indeed. But the image of Andy Boyd—more heard than seen—as if careening around a curve in a 1955 Dodge on two wheels with tires screaming—checked him. Reminded him. He had understood perfectly—this was at the graveside, when he had decided to forego the amenities and the clichés—that she could not be allowed to stay out her time in Peegram; that she would have to leave town, not two weeks from now but immediately. This was a fact superseding irony, standing clear of it and all else, all wishes and all fears. And though it mocked him in every way, there was nothing to be done—the solid fact remained. He might cry out in agony, *Give us just these two weeks, God, we won't ask for more,* and the fact would not be moved. He might measure the two weeks in the very terms he had thought he so loathed—in lingering looks and secret meetings and knees touching under tables and hasty caresses —to no purpose. And it meant (all his life was lost; the holy of holies forever and ever lost) and it meant, it did mean that he was saving himself, chapter and verse of the blameless life, all his argument upon respectability, his proud name and his pastorate. Whatever it meant, the fact stood: she had to go. . . . He knew he could not leave Peegram. Could he have asked her to stay and continued the argument that way? Leaving the church; leaving his wife; replying, finally, thus. (Ah, my father.) He did not know and would never know when Andy Boyd and his sort made such a consideration only a dream.

The pressure of his love was intolerable, but he did not touch her. She was too young to be touched, kissed, and loved, and then immediately sent packing. Was he right? He wished the damn car did not make their breathing seem so loud and so anguished and so mingled; he could not distinguish her breathing from his.

"You can't wait till May thirtieth to leave town," he told her.

"What did you say?"

He said it again, adding, "You will have to leave town at once."

"I'll do no such thing!" she said.

"You must. There's too much chance of a . . . mess. There's a pretty rough bunch out to get you. They could run you down with a car. Produce an 'accident' in the school supply room—in your grade room, almost anywhere. You must go."

"But the funeral's over and there wasn't any trouble. And Roger drives me to school and back and I don't go to town any more and . . ."

It was his turn to say "Roger!" but he had neither the will nor the heart. "That's not enough. If something happened to you, don't you see, it would be worse for the children than seeing you leave ahead of schedule."

"But they'll think I'm a coward—they'll think I've run out, which will be exactly what I'll have done if . . ."

He reeled it off rapidly, exactly as if he had it all memorized: "You can tell them you've been *asked* to leave early. I'll take the responsibility for that. They know you're no coward. We'll get a substitute teacher—Mrs. Webb, you'll approve of her and the children know her, they had her, off and on, last year. You can go over the records with her and for the most part make out the report cards yourself. Two weeks isn't going to make a great difference in their standing. I'll call Roger about it right away. We'll arrange that you see Mrs. Webb this afternoon, tonight. At your rooming house. I don't want you out in this interval. We'll get the things you'll need from the school on our way back to town. Then you can pack and finish up tomorrow—Sunday—tell the kids good-by Monday morning and be out of town by Monday noon at the latest. . . ."

He need not tell her that he would also hire some plain-clothes men from Madison to watch the rooming house, or of the one or two other things that he would see to. She was looking full at him but he could not look at her. Fact was fact, but irony was also irony, and he did not blame her that the quarrel took a new turn. This last role of his—this being the one "to encourage her out of town"—was one he could have done without. Involuntarily, his eyes cut to the rear-view mirror where the rotting cabin was, by the rules of the heart, so unaccountably still reflected.

She was blazing. "You're sure—you're absolutely positive —that my leaving is necessary."

"I'm positive."

"All right," she breathed. "You win."

One, turn on the ignition. Two, step on the starter. Three, put the gear in reverse. He did not move.

"I'm a stranger, I'm not 'of you.' I'm never to understand 'what happened,' I'm never to know. I can be patronized and dismissed!"

"I'm sorry if it seems as harsh as all that. This whole thing has been extremely rough on you, I know. But . . . you do have to leave. That's the sum of it."

"Suppose I refuse to leave in ignorance. Suppose I say I have the right to know."

To know what? She was superb in anger, very vulnerable and very proud. Very womanlike too. If he had asked her what it was she wanted so much to know, she would have spread her hands and answered, "Everything." He glanced at the dashboard clock. Could he make her know about love in the hour, and not hurt her forever? It wasn't just that she was so young, she was a virgin. He had guessed as much when she was telling him about the education degree, known for certain when the whole landscape became nothing but eyes. His heart beat wildly, wildly anticipating. To think that he would not be ashamed of his tenderness! . . . And if he guessed that he was rather wide of the mark; that it was not specifically, in the moment, a knowledge of love she longed for but a knowledge of "everything," the whole dark secret of the past, so that, again womanlike, she might have, in love, "everything," dark and bright, with all the tragic overtones of this bright and particular Saturday in proper perspective; if he guessed, he still had a sense of the constriction of time, which she did not; an understanding that "everything" was juxtaposed with "nothing." But he should not have been so thrown off when she said, "Who is it your son takes after, since it is not you? Who is it William Morrison hearkens back to?" Yet he was distracted by the familiar, slow-working coldness rising in him at the mention of his son.

She went on. "Why did Ray . . . ? What about Carrie? Why did she . . . ? What about . . . ?" Looking all around, at the sky and the mountains, very much as he had done. "There was a question I was told not to ask again if I expected to get out of town in one piece. Maybe I don't want to get out of town in one piece, maybe that's it." Laughing, almost hysterically.

Again, distracted. Defining it in love's terms: of course, she would not get out of town "in one piece." But their misunderstanding was now way out of bounds, the question turning out to be "Who was Harry Hibbard?" No doubt, he *was* forewarned!

PART TWO

Full fathom five thy father lies;
  Of his bones are coral made;
Those are pearls that were his eyes:
  Nothing of him that doth fade,
But doth suffer a sea-change
  Into something rich and strange.
Sea-nymphs hourly ring his knell . . .

Harry Hibbard

1

THAT AUGUST—THE AUGUST HARRY HIBBARD WAS DROWNED—
Peegram lay drugged with heat, which was, as Peegramites
kept insisting when they could summon the energy, "unusual." The Peegram climate, they said, was noted for its
mildness. But this heat was of the solid sort, with storms
unable to come to a head, though a storm was always somewhere in the offing. Sounds did not seem to travel but to
drop heavily into the earth, and the only sound that seemed
capable of rising was the strange, wild, dry cry of the cicadas.
In Peegram there had been no drop of rain for two and one-
half weeks.

The river may have shrunk but it added its burden to the
atmosphere. It was there; you could taste it on the tongue
and find it oozing out through the glands. The funky dank-

ness of it was on the air, commingling—conniving—with the dust, as if to hold the dust in permanent suspension. The town hung in dust. The old maple trees on Front Street sagged—affected the color of the dust—were inert. A dog went mad, running the unwavering course of its madness at high noon, down Front Street. Except that Seth Erwin was named Man of the Year by the Chamber of Commerce, this was the only happening, the only news since the heat had settled in. Seth Erwin and the dog shared the Peegram *Inquirer's* front-page honors. (There was a picture of the dog too.) And Peegram was waiting in a state of dull expectancy for better relief than the thoughts of the dog and Seth Erwin had afforded; waiting for a storm to come and purge the environment thoroughly. When:

When on one especially heavy day during this heavy August, a car, a light tan Oldsmobile, came speeding over the flat, almost barren land, heading for Peegram. The driver of the car was Harry Hibbard. Peegram was his destination. Traveling for Royall Furniture, he had been away on one of his regular selling trips and was now on his way back. The artificial wind from the ventilator windows was hot in his face, his sweat-wet shirt was molded to his body, his coat was on the seat beside him, but he came as a knight in shining armor, that day; as a hero, that day, with a mission. The blue-looking highway shimmered in the sun; he both watched and did not watch it. (When he was born, they put him behind a steering wheel and said, "Drive.") Not a bird called or a cloud moved. The car consumed mile after mile. A brown rabbit skittered across the highway, glancing back over the white-balled tip of its behind.

"Tibbar," Harry muttered.

.And he had developed this backward language to relieve the tedium of the road. A rabbit was a tibbar, a cow a woc, a roof a foor; speed limit became deeps timil. "Doog gnin-rom," he had caught himself on the verge of saying to the bellhop this morning. Of course he had his games—cow poker, woc rekop, and bets on the number of television antennae between towns, always paying himself off. Once, he swore, he had seen one atop a privy. Even his counting was done in this language now, eno, owt, eerht. His mind was apt to fill up with backward-computed statistics of graveyards, fence posts, advertising slogans. . . . Though not that day; his notation of the tibbar was purely automatic that day; his mind was actively exploring the geography of Carrie—Eirrac —that day, as well as feeling out toward his younger boy, Ray, whom he did not designate as Yar, for some reason, ever. He would not think of counting sheep to put himself to sleep; he would count peehs, eno, owt, eerht . . .

But his occupation had left more than this one quirk in him. He had a surprising knowledge of the Bible, garnered from all the Gideon Bibles in all the hotel rooms. In the main, when the day's work was concluded, he had concerned himself with that, with the Bible, rather than with whiskey and women—another quirk, surely. For a decade, now, when he was at home at Peegram between trips, he had immediately taken himself off again to the river and to the cabin he had built, for fishing, for hunting, as the season allowed. For a decade, this had been his way of life. He had supposed it was good enough for him until one of Seth's strange sermons had cast him high and dry with the question of how long he was going to continue to run away. "Come home," the sermon said, "and save us from her. Wasn't that the agreement?

Didn't you swear, long ago, to dare the labyrinth and the monster, for our sake? And didn't you imply that you, you hero, were the only man who was man enough? And didn't you imply even more than that, you arrogant bastard: that if a man was man enough, she wouldn't turn out to be a monster at all but a woman-true? A fine kettle of fish," the sermon said, "with her rampant and *you* hiding in hotels and the woods!"

And the beginning of it was that never had Harry put in a claim for possessing himself, for selfhood. It seemed to him, for what reasons he was unable to divine, that he had always been public property, like a railroad station rest room. ("Play ball," they told him when he was born.) He couldn't remember when they had not said, "Harry, better watch that knee, son." "Come on, Harry, damn it, carry that ball over!—What you waiting for, a streetcar?" "What's the matter, Harry, old pal, old pal, hole in the wood?" "Ah, Harry, no cigarettes for you!" Then, with the war, hadn't they made him wear a squashed cap and silver wings above his heart, when his own dim inclination was the infantry? Hadn't they made it clear enough that his role in life, his duty, was to content them? And made it also clear, although not quite so clear, that he might have contented them better had he come home flag-draped? He was theirs, he did not dispute it, and he had always obeyed them, though why this obedience was exacted of him he did not know. The war was all that had prevented them from making him go pro (for there had been scouts and what scouts! they were never tired, even now, of recollecting), so that they might chew over his career with the Dodgers or the Indians for years. Still, heroes were supposed to be moribund at forty and Harry would never see his fortieth birthday again. And if for the past decade he had played the fox with them, he would have said he had nevertheless only recently reached the margin of real safety. He was no poolroom philosopher, had no desire to recapture the past, simply to escape it. Oh, he knew he would have to take a backward glance at it through Fred, Harry Frederick Hibbard, Jr., his older boy, who, as everybody said, was Harry's spittin' image and would have to be a hero too, a fact which saddened him. But he would have said he had earned his own retirement at last. When:

When: *Come on home, Harry, and save us from her.* The voice of Seth, though it was more complicated than that, to do Seth justice, and, as a crisis, had been building up—well, for this decade which dated (there was no getting around it) from the birth of Ray, or (looked at from another vantage point) from the death of Carrie's mother Flora and old Zeb Erwin.

As in all other things, he had obeyed them in the matter of his marriage. Nor had he seen any particular point in trying to make it evident to them that he had also happened to love her. Their curiosity and their fear would not have been able to endure that. And he did not remind them that he was the boy, in the third grade, who had tripped her up and banged her over the head with his book satchel (those unmistakable third-grade signs of love, at least when he was growing up). Long before he asked her—even during high school years when he was having his fling with all those slick little blond chicks—he knew he would marry her. And it had pleased him to lift up the bridal veil (a veil of hurt; that was what *they* had done to her, hurt her)—to lift it up and find the pioneer woman, as he had known he would. He used to fancy her

turning enormous flapjacks, while holding off the Indians
with a musket poked carelessly out a knothole, a picture that
far from repelling him stirred his desire from the depths. Far
better to take her than some feeble little wench, squeaking
and clinging to the male at the sight of a mouse. All power
and silence and shyness—she moved him. A woman, by the
Lord, a whole continent of woman. She was nearly as big as
he was. And nearly as lonely, Abel Erwin's daughter, as
Harry Hibbard who was everybody's son; nearly as astonished by tenderness; and—he had to smile, because they had
broken down two not-in-the-least rickety beds—far more
astonished than he by their passion. The deprivation of the
war years (which separated Fred from Ray) was almost
more than they could bear. . . . She used to come and stand
behind his chair; he would knock out his pipe and fold the
newspaper, with loud crackles, lengthwise, before getting to
his feet and beginning the ascent upstairs; he never looked
back at her. . . . The night he deflowered her, she had
fought him like a fiend. She had *demanded* conquering.

And she had demanded sons! (He used to worry lest a
dainty little daughter make her appearance. Because, as he
had seemed to understand, she would not be tolerated for a
moment.) Without sons, there would be disaster, as he had
fairly early sensed, since her womb was the strong and tire-
less sort destined to repopulate the earth (Peegram, of
course). At the very least, five sons, and seven if the weather
had held, as the song said, but really, and preferably, twelve.
The round of that womb was the world; the flat of that womb
would be hell, because of all the energy that would become
deflected, distorted into a grievous different phantom-shape
and a phantom-shape which (yes) had always threatened,

but a shape which—while it was the womb's prerogative to gestate it and bring it forth as standard equipment of sons— was still not, by God, standard equipment of the woman, except in sickened imagination, where it was phantom in- deed, and so must be endlessly and savagely pursued. Oh, yes, he had known! He was the man—let Seth mock—who had taken the dare. That was so. He had placed his bets upon himself.

The car sped on, consuming the miles, but obligated, as it was, to following the blue-looking road rather than trying a course possibly more its own. Speaking in his private, back- ward language, he said, "I ma gniog emoh"—I am going home. "Irrevocably," the road replied.

Well, and Fred had come ten and one-half months after nuptials. On schedule, and as fine a specimen as anybody could have desired. (Fine little old standard equipment too.) Nobody could help the war—and he had made it back, at that, before it was over. They met the schedule again—hard on!—in eleven months, on the button, this time. And they were a closed corporation, Carrie and what she carried, and Fred, and him. He would never forget the day she told him, "I am with child." Even her way of holding her shoulders was different. In those days Carrie would about as soon have attended a committee or a board of directors' meeting as he would a chippie house or a cock fight. In those days she canned peaches and pushed around an old upright vacuum cleaner with a bag on it, and hummed tunes under her breath, and sewed, and marked damn near every day's end by coming to stand behind his chair (up and through the seventh month), and those days, or rather those nights, Harry was always at home, he was working in the Royall

plant and had not yet hit the road. (Harry did not start working for Royall until after he was mustered out of the Air
Corps; in other words, not until well after Abel's death, and
not until after Zeb and Flora had, for all practical purposes,
thrown Royall away. It was early clearer to some than to
others that Carrie was never going to inherit it.)

Ray was not premature, though he did look like some old
man's joke when he was born—Harry granted that. Carrie
knew Flora was dying even as she was giving birth—telegrams kept arriving and Carrie was not the sort you hid the
contents of telegrams from. Flora's death was hourly expected as Carrie's labors, much more difficult than with Fred,
continued from one hour to the next, as if without end. At
the time, Harry was not even sure Carrie knew about Flora
and old Zeb's carrying on. He was not able to follow Carrie's
reading of the telegrams, let alone her reading of birth and
death as they were confused in her feverish mind. "She's
done it!" she could cry. And he did not know what it was
that she had done. He recalled the ghastly scream announcing Ray's arrival—it had brought the sweat out all over him—
it had echoed up and down the corridor where he was standing. It was when she waked from the deep sleep that followed
that she announced that Ray was not her son. "She does
know about Flora and Zeb," had been Harry's reading of this.
Ray was not hers, he was a punishment, a cross laid on her.
He was the fruit of that other union someway visited on
her; sin that had skipped a generation. Of course, Harry
should have sensed how serious it was, but he didn't. He
thought it was the combination of shock and hysteria and
that she would get over it. He thought that that big quiet
woman's pride of hers was hurt but that she would come

around. Besides, his own reaction to Ray was so different. Upon his first sight of him, he had hastened down the corridor and out the door in a straight route to increase his insurance policies. (He had not, as he had done with Fred, bought cigars to distribute and gone around with his chest out.) Thinking—he could remember it just as well as if it were yesterday—"Why, he's the saddest, funniest little morsel of humanity I've ever seen—he'll never amount to a hill of beans!" Happy about it too. Alone-happy. Feeling of relief all through him. Of course, he had to ask himself, why *was* he so relieved—so pleased? Why did he suddenly feel like a rich man? Why did he feel free? It wasn't such a mystery. It was because he was giving the world something the world had no rules for and no use for. And of course it pleased him mightily! The world never would possess this son—it didn't know how. And he—Harry—was going to see to it that this son could go his useless way with dollars in his pocket. He remembered, he had tried to tell Seth as much, inasmuch as it seemed obvious Ray came from Seth's, rather than Carrie's side of the Erwins, if indeed he came from anywhere other than God's bosom. Harry had loved Ray in that special way a man can only love that which he deems worthless, unessential and extraneous to himself; that which he feels he cannot possibly use toward satisfying his own secret or open ambitions—or convert—or exploit. No need involved, no obligation. Absolutely, the profit motive out of it. Without Fred, Harry realized, he might not have been able to bear the sight of Ray; but with Fred, Ray was the apple of his eye. Time was when he had tried to tell himself that that was all right, an equitable enough distribution, since Fred was so obviously the apple of Carrie's eye. There was enough love to go around, and then some, because there would be more, and yet more, sons. But Ray spelled the beginning of the end. Carrie was never the same again. Carrie and Ray were not out of the hospital when Flora's dying ended in death, old Zeb's trailing by a week. At the primitive, woman level of Carrie's mind there must have been an enormous churning. Together these two had violated her womb, making of it their own dirty joke—was that it?—but now, that was not the whole of the joke, it would seem, since it became certain that together they had robbed her of her entire inheritance, with the exception of—just to make sure she got the point of the joke—that one damned Persian rug, which Harry wished he had taken personally and thrown in the river. Not that that could have made the difference, once she was on the loose; dimes just did turn into dollars under her touch. It was Harry's sneaking suspicion she could have made her pile out of what she saved from the always too-generous housekeeping allowance he gave her; that, in fact, and in plain arithmetic, he'd probably be shocked to know the profits she had managed for herself out of it, and without cutting corners either, and him never thinking to ask for an accounting.

It was some time before he could take it in: that the woman in Carrie had turned to stone; that that wonderful womb would never quicken again!

He built his cabin, he hit the road. He came into his compromise (like an inheritance too): Gideon Bibles and hotels, the woods, the river, the fields. Armed retreat with gun and rod and reel. He spread out the map of his loneliness, smoothing the creases most painstakingly. A year passed. Then, in a burst of conscience, like the captain of some ship who realizes

that really his ship has sprung a leak and is sinking, though
the sea lies so calm, he made Carrie go to Doc Claywell and
he went himself. Doc made tests and examinations and said
nothing was wrong. He winked at Harry and told him to
come home oftener. Another year passed before he would
allow that the ship was indeed resting on the bottom and
could only be classified as a wreck. Hopeless.

And, meanwhile, there began to be rumors of Carrie's doings to which Harry would not listen. Because it was crystal
clear that if he had taken to the woods, she had moved out on
the town. Not money in itself, but power, of course, was her
aim. All innocence, she began asking him to affix his signature
to papers he was too proud to read through before so doing.
Soon this became ritual; he told himself he did not care. That
it was not his concern if she was making a million out of wild-
cat Kansas oil wells with the purpose of throwing her weight
around in Peegram. None of it was what he wanted. He made
straight money and plenty of it and that was good enough for
him; it had once been good enough for her. And would he
deny that he had enjoyed being such an adequate and generous provider for Abel Erwin's daughter? No. He knew it
had meant a lot to him; he knew he hadn't been sorry a bit
when it had looked like she was poor. He would always take
care of her. Right along, he had carried a lot of insurance; he
did now. . . . Which year was it they started making out
separate income tax returns? The same year they started
sleeping in separate beds and bedrooms? . . . The house
was as efficiently run as ever; more so. It wasn't gadget-
crazy, but it was decidedly gadget-complete. And never was
there any omission when he came home—to hang his hat;

to change his traps—of beer in the refrigerator for him. There was a layer of politeness a foot thick. And the telephone rang constantly (for her).

And, meanwhile, Ray stayed puny. He hated milk (an insult to any mother). He didn't distinguish himself in anything—either in cute sayings or in pretty manners or in Boy Scouts or in school. Harry, of course, hadn't expected he would. But Carrie thought differently. If she was going to withhold love from Ray and regard him, in her secret heart, as a curse, it was very important to her that nobody ever be able to point the finger of blame. Nobody should ever be able to say she had neglected him or discriminated against him. Therefore it followed, as the night does the day, that what they were to say was, how well he was turning out, by Peegram's standards, and thanks to Carrie. Ray *had* to reflect to Carrie's credit. That was that. If not exactly an easy task or easy material to work with. Harry remembered the piano-practicing periods, Ray doodling around in the high notes. His solution was to take the cat in with him and keep her chasing a string up and down the keys, so that for a couple of days Carrie (who had no ear) thought he was showing great improvement and rewarded him accordingly. Carrie worked on a system of rewards, as if training a retriever. Every night Carrie would hear Ray's prayers, and it came out that Ray was not saying his prayers properly. Kneeling by his bed, with his hands meekly folded, what he was really chanting was, "Chile is pur-ple and China is yellow." (He liked maps.) As a substitute for "God bless Mama and God bless Daddy," Carrie thought nothing of this. She "rewarded" him into "Now I lay me" and left it at that.

He liked maps! But was that an achievement? Something

Peegram folks set store in? He liked to read in their old
Encyclopaedia Britannica, but only when it rained, and it
would take a climate of rainy seasons to get any knowledge
that would impress Peegram folks into him. He liked to play
games of make-believe with little Polly Taylor from across
the street, a skinny, bedraggled little girl who would seem to
have very little to recommend her. As Carrie moved out on
the town, it was perhaps curious that compliments on her
husband and sons was the tribute she exacted. Everybody
knew this. Everybody knew the way to open negotiations
with her was to praise Harry and Fred and Ray in a row. It
had to be got out of the way first, like the subjects kissing the
Caesar's foot and declaring how sweet it smelled before getting around to intrigue. Carrie did not allow praise to be
beamed directly upon herself. But if there was *nothing* to say
about Ray, it was both embarrassing and conducive to considerable strain, since Carrie would not let them off any more
than she would Ray. And it became increasingly evident that
Ray *had* to be outstanding in something Peegram could latch
onto, she didn't care what.

Harry was not sure when his worry about Ray began to be
explicit. Or when it was he began to ask himself with greater
frequency: could his own love for the boy outbalance his
mother's lack of it, particularly when he was so seldom
around? Ray was a high-strung, mercurial sort of child, with
many joys (and, perhaps, many fears). He never seemed to
Harry to be quite real and it was odd that Harry, more often
than not, felt abashed in his presence. He would want to
draw close to the boy, yet his instinct was to leave him strictly
to his own devices. Ray would pirouette through a room and
if you asked him where he was going, he might say, "Oh, to

Madagascar." Or to the moon—but in no standard space-ship
way of little boys, Harry felt. Or to the foot of the rainbow.
And he would have nothing whatsoever to do with grownups; he avoided them like the plague. And when Carrie
showed him off, to collect her compliments, he would sometimes wet his pants. His hair was as soft and almost as white
as on the day he was born and his eyes were the color of
violets. His features were so finely adjusted that he resembled
one of those Greek statues, Harry thought, or maybe a poem.
And since Harry was no poem and the kid was no athlete
(with those matchstick arms and legs), Harry's attitude toward him, as he himself knew, was a little too reverent. One
time—this would have been when Ray was about three—he
came pirouetting up to Harry and said, "Cherish me, Daddy."
Harry, amazed: where had he learned that word? He picked
him up and held him close; hugged him. "Is this what you
mean?" "Yes," Ray said. Sometimes, even yet, when he was
least expecting it, Ray would materialize and say, "Cherish
me, Daddy," and of course it had become a ceremony, hugging him, and running his hand through that strangely soft
hair. . . . It was Seth who said to him one day (Seth; always
Seth!), "I'm glad he isn't mine." They were sitting on the
porch idly watching Ray and Seth's boy, William Morrison,
playing in the yard. Harry took offense. "By God, I'm proud
to call him mine." Then Seth said, with that gentleness that
was apt to come on him when you were most ready to slit his
throat, "He'd scare me, that's all." Harry wanted to come
back with, "He's *like* you, that's all. You danced around and
wet your pants. You looked like an angel too. And I would
wonder plenty of times where you had dropped from." If
Elaine had been in the hospital with William Morrison at the

same time Carrie was with Ray, Harry might have thought
there had been a mix-up of the nursery tags. But as hard as it
was to believe, what with William Morrison's being so much
sturdier and bigger, he was three or four months the younger
of the two.

The thought began to occur and reoccur to Harry: if he let
Carrie destroy that child, he would never be able to forgive
himself! And he began to see the child's puny grace that he
had once taken such detached pleasure in with a new narrow-
ing of the eyes. What was going to stop Carrie from destroying him? It was almost as if (the thought gave him a
curious twist in his bowels) Carrie and Seth had committed
spiritual incest—he put that thought away fast! The boy
seemed so lost sometimes, so hard up against Carrie's indif-
ference, as it combined with her demands. And since it was
the freedom of finding himself that Harry would have given
him from the beginning, what was to be done? Probably he
ought to spend more time with the kid, get to know him,
overcome his own shyness, draw him out, give him a hand
up. He began to see it as his duty to get over the impulse to
leave him be. He hadn't known where or how to start, but
maybe . . . fishing . . . hunting. (Fred had been going
with him, off and on, since he was eight.) And with that
grace and quickness, who could tell? Harry was hopeful
about it, wondering why he hadn't thought of it sooner, and
Ray seemed to be delighted by the prospect. But it was a
mistake. Harry made a discovery that kept him awake nights.
He discovered that all Ray's graceful movements culminated,
with a regularity that was frightening, in disaster. It was
most curious—Harry didn't understand it and had never seen
anything quite like it. Ray would come, running lightly down

the stone steps from the cabin, minnow bucket and pole in hand. "Take it easy, son," Harry would call. "Don't run." Ray was too excited ever to hear such warnings. On he would come—lightly, gracefully, swiftly—only to crash down the last step and end sprawling, with hook perhaps one inch from eye. This had not happened once, but it or something like it had happened almost every time Harry took him out. Not only did it fail to afford them common ground, but it made things worse, since Ray's inability to handle himself in no way interfered with his desire to fish, which grew stronger every time he nearly killed himself. So that, ironically enough, Harry found he was reduced to slipping away from the house when Ray was not around, and telling Fred, if Fred were going, to meet him down at the corner. But it was no help—not to have to hear Ray's sobs at being left behind, or see him visiting Maggie, the bird-dog bitch, in her backyard pen, and breaking rules by opening the gate and going in *there*, for comfort and love! As for hunting, that was completely out, though Fred had been given his single-shot .22 rifle on his ninth birthday. From a window Harry watched Ray stalking sparrows with a sawed-off broomstick, heard his "pow-pow-pow" and saw him pitch over into the holly bush with the end of the broomstick buried in his stomach. For Ray's sake, Harry revamped his cabin schedule. When he was in town, he spent all his nights at home, making it a point to be back in time for late dinner. It had cost him some, because he had come to depend on nights at the cabin with the pines and the stars.

The car had been relentlessly consuming the miles, and, almost imperceptibly, the contours of the land had changed—it was no longer flat, but undulating. There were curves and dips in the road. There were many small farms—now, parched fields—and long stretches of woods, heat-heavy and bedraggled. Home territory. . . .

It was not until his last time home that Harry had heard Seth's sermon. But it was also this same time home that something else had happened. A carnival was in town. Naturally the boys had planned to go. But there was a polio scare and neither he nor Carrie wanted them mixing in a crowd. Harry explained it carefully to them, why they were not being allowed to go. Then he went off to the river for the day with Jim. When he came back in time for late dinner, he discovered that the boys had slipped off and had themselves a fine old carnival time. When he was home, matters of discipline were in his hands. (He suspected that when he was away, there weren't any.) Fred, at fifteen, was too old to whip—Harry hadn't touched him since he was twelve. But he had an unreasonable, panicky fear of polio, and at the sight of Fred, looking so husky and unbothered, in his dirty T-shirt, and with that damned pink cotton candy smeared all over his mug, Harry lost his temper. The picture blurred and he saw Fred a cripple dragging his shrunken limbs around in braces. Harry took him up to his room and went for the leather strap he had used to use on him in a sort of trance and hit him with it once, across the shoulders, before coming to his senses. Fred stood eying him, with his face flushed, and flushing deeper.

"Get out," Harry said, instead of apologizing. How many times had his own father raised the welts on him? How many times—and why?—had he gotten up again, when every bone in his body felt crushed, adjusting his helmet? He knew Fred was doomed; he had always been hard on him.

The door closed. Harry sank into a chair and fumbled for a cigarette. He felt he had behaved abominably; yet he felt the undefinable shape of love in the room. The door opened. Ray came in, came inching along the wall, with his hands held behind him. The strap was still lying on the floor in plain view.

"I did it, too," Ray said.

He had to repeat it, Harry supposed, in his thin, sweet voice that was trembling so.

"Yes," Harry said gently. "But you're much younger. He talked you into it."

"No, he didn't," Ray said, standing with his back to the wall. "*I* talked *him* into it. I even paid our way."

Harry drew hard on his cigarette.

"You whipped him. You have to whip me too."

"All right," Harry said, after a long pause, and not arguing the point.

He made Ray get over the arm of the overstuffed chair. He had never so much as spanked him. He put out his cigarette and leaned down for the strap and straightened with the strap in his hand and brought it down over Ray's behind— God knew, not with any force. But it seemed to him that Ray's scream tore the heart of the house out. Numbly, he stood there, trying to think what was to be done next. He brought the strap down a second time. The second scream made the first as far away as a memory. He stood there, dazed. Then it was as if his whole self got involved in a terrible upheaval, and as if a voice wrenched itself loose and broke clear through and out of him: *My son!* The strap rose and fell several times, to make it more tragic, or more complete, or more final, this act of recognition. The strap slipped from his hand at almost the same instant that Ray slipped to the floor in a heap, wildly sobbing.

He heard Carrie's footsteps on the stairs. He stood back, stood off, waiting for her. Let her lift him up. It was the father who must train the son to courage (the backward answer to cowardice) and the mother who must come along and kiss away the tears the father's lesson leaves behind. . . . He even hoped she would accuse him: "What have you done to our child?" He did not question it at all, but thought it marvelous, that his own recognition had spread to her. He heard her feet steady in the hall. She never walked faster and she never walked slower. That was no useless plaything on the floor at his feet, nothing he could afford to throw away in revenge against those who had made the rules he had spent his life in over-obeying. That quivering, terrified little heap was the second part of his answer to Man and God.

Carrie came in. She crossed the room, stepping around the sobbing boy, and closed the window. She went out again.

2

. . . . Mackerel sky, but it wasn't going to rain. *She closed the window!* He slid his sweating hands along the steering wheel.

No, Seth. I don't come to save *you* from her. I come to save *her* . . . from you . . . from *them,* the *they* that means Peegram to me. Ten years late. O.K. But I'm coming *today.* For Carrie's and Fred's and Ray's and my sake, see? And the only thing you nailed down right was that I was hiding out, running away. So let's get that straight, Seth. We aren't playing on the same team. And if I bag Carrie and you come crawling up to offer me your congratulations in the name of the good town of Peegram, watch out. I wanted to hit you that time you came slinking in with her to the senior dance —I may do it yet.

He had caught the old girl's scent again on a high wind, the old girl who as a young girl had had to fight him like a fiend before giving in. *She closed the window!* The boy's sobs were poor publicity. He set that against "*My son!*" And not that it was a tragedy generating out of the moment rather than the years, but that it was the moment in which it all came clear to him; in which he put on responsibility like an old discarded coat he had hoped was threadbare. And when his rage had slacked off and he thought he had his desire to kill her under control, he found out it wasn't in him to kill her—he didn't want to kill her, any more than he wanted a divorce— he wanted to save her too. It was terrible, in a way, to admit you loved the woman who had done what she had done to their son and in almost the same breath with his own utmost recognition of the son himself. But he guessed he saw it in her as sickness and not as evil. The sickness for which he was still the cure. That meant he had to try to salvage their perfectly ordered wreck of a home.

Yeah . . . he was coming in to that narrower field where the quarry had always been. Carrie didn't know it yet, but he was coming home for good. Royall Furniture didn't know it yet, but he was going to take them up on the job of sales manager they had been after him about ever since Billy Slade had had his coronary—nigh on a year ago now—and which had forced Billy to slow down to the point of retirement.

Harry wasn't going to travel any more, not as he had been.
(Other than going to markets, the Royall sales manager didn't
do much traveling. His assistant and district sales managers
did most of the trouble shooting involving the traveling, except insofar as the biggest accounts were concerned.) He
wasn't going to allow himself to get anywhere near the river;
he wouldn't open the cabin. No more of that—not, at least,
until it stopped meaning escape. And Carrie . . . well, Carrie was going to quit her shenanigans. He thought he had a
nodding acquaintance with the guy who could make her. He
might have to jerk the phone out by its roots and keep her
locked up, on bread and water, for a while. Might even have
to run the town himself for a while just to show her. Might
have to beat her at some deal. Beat her at her own game. And
if they should grind each other into fine powder? The hell
with that. Let the trumpets sound.

He grinned—he came armed, didn't he? He had a globe for
Ray that lit up from within at the push of an electric button—
Chile was decidedly purple. He had some records that a nice
lady in a music store had helped him to pick out, one of these
being "Peter and the Wolf." He had some books, some for
Ray and some for himself. He had a copy of the Bible, the
King James version, Gideon version. It had hardly occurred
to him that it might be possible to make himself over a little,
or find some new layers in himself he hadn't known about, on
the boy's account. Athletics hadn't left him much time in his
younger days for doing much else. He thought it was curious
that in order to find out what his boy—what the poem was
really all about, he would have to find it first in his own guts.
He shifted his weight restlessly. For Fred he had brought the

new creel and the lures. For Carrie—a nightgown with a lot of lace on it. "In the biggest size you've got," he had told the girl.

He could not see it, or hear it, but the river was now on his left, three hundred yards beyond the file of jackpine. For a second, his mind filled with the sight of his line going out over the water. In fishing, in hunting, you killed what you loved. You killed the fish and the birds. Killing was an intimate, binding, sacred act. Every hunter and every fisherman knew that, though he might not know why. The sound of the wind in the tops of the trees around his cabin seemed to sough through Harry's mind. Ray couldn't joint up a rod or take a gun in hand without someway turning the sacred act of killing on himself. Not that he had the slightest awareness of what he was doing; it just seemed to be a kind of condition of his hands and feet, his flesh and bones. But it seemed suddenly, and so strangely, to be his own condition also, that Harry began to watch the road with attention. He had caught so many fish, brought down so many, many birds in his time. And men as well, if he must count the war. Was the act of killing a man a violation of the sacred? What was the difference? This was one of the questions he had put to the Gideon Bible again and again. Death *was* sacred to life since you had to be willing to contain death in you—the death of birds and beasts and fish and vegetables—in order to live, contain it and defecate it back; that was both the condition and the proposition (death *was* life); sensing which, the killing of a bird involved tenderness, and humility, and faith in your own worth. You had to *be* worth it, not trying to *believe* you were worth it by way of a pack of lies. But men didn't eat each other, not since cannibal days anyhow.

A man could not eat the man he was told to kill, and he could not eat himself, and so there was a line drawn that nature seemed to approve. "Integrity of the species"—wasn't that what it was called? But maybe that had to do with mating, not killing. . . . And the Lord's Supper, the proffered Body and the proffered Blood—they were surely symbolic. (But symbolic of *what*?)

There was the day, early in the war, when he had lost Peanut Robinette, his wingman. The same burst of flak had got the wing of his own plane, which was on fire, though miraculously he himself was not even bruised. He had watched the ragged flame eating along the metal of the wing, rib by rib. It was the first nightmare of Peanut burning—the two were to stay confused in his mind, his dreams punning on "wing" and "man," to this day. But he sat there watching the ragged flame eating its way, rib by rib, and it was as if nothing had ever happened of all that had happened afterward, and that he was still sitting there, in the sky, with his dull, furious hope riveted to the flame's progress.

Sign ahead:

PEEGRAM CITY LIMITS
BIRD SANCTUARY 1935

"Margeep Ytic Stimil," Harry muttered. "Drib Yrautcnas 5391."

It gave him a jolt as it always did: Peegram. As if all the roads in the world led back to it. Even now, in the heat and the dust, announcing itself. Suppose the dense center of Carrie's purpose was Harry's unmanning. . . . As hot as it was, he shivered.

Front Street. The courthouse. The courthouse bums sitting along the low stone retaining wall, in the dappled shade, as always. They waved to him; they knew him. He waved back. One would lean forward and spit and say to the one next, "Remember that time old Harry pitched against Moravia? . . ." Or maybe they'd argue it out, once more, whether it was baseball or football he had played best. That could occupy them, chapter and verse, for a solid hour. "Nope. No, sir, Colonel, you forgit professional football didn't figure, those days, like it does now. That's how come them baseball scouts was all we heard about. Choo-Choo Justice? My foot—I tell you, Harry Hibbard was the greatest back ever trotted onto a field. They don't come like him no more. Tough—offensive—defensive—in there the whole game, boy, those were the days. Fast. And how he could hit a line, Colonel. Why, he couldn't hit *no* line without pickin' up five yards. I'll never forgit that time . . ." Then the statistics, games, scores, the first downs, the fumbles and the recoveries, the completed passes (who had passed to whom) and the incompleted passes . . . endless. And why? Why did it matter? What if you had that kind of memory for the fumbles and the recoveries of your own heart, or soul, or whatever it was? Where would you be then?

He had stopped for the light. Jesse Tate was crossing the square. "Hey, Harry," Jesse called. "Hi, Jess," Harry called back. "Good to see you home, son." "Thanks." The light changed. "It's good to be here."

The length of Front Street he was waved to and called to and he waved back and called back. They knew him, he knew them. . . . Jim and Jimbo were coming out of Lambeth's, but did not see him, though he honked his horn to attract their attention. It was probably just as well. It was probably better if Jim didn't know, at least for a while, that he was back. It would be too hard to explain why he wasn't going near the river or even opening the cabin. Jim would understand his preferring to do his fishing alone for a spell. With each, that often happened. But Jim would not understand his not going fishing at all!

He turned into Mimosa Avenue, main artery of niggertown, in order to cut over to what some folks liked to designate as Erwin Heights, the fancy "new" residential section, where, on Rabbit Road (Harry was stubbornly responsible for that name), there stood a house, modified Colonial, he believed.

3

Fred, in bringing Harry a beer, said something about the lures (these lures were honeys; one of them Harry had been looking for for two years) and about their taking off in the morning for the cabin. Harry told him he wasn't planning to go out to the cabin.

He thought Fred would show surprise—perhaps even concern for his father's health—but Fred merely teetered back on his heels and asked permission, in that case, to repair there himself, with some of his friends; he said he was sure Coach Perkins would be glad to make one of the party.

"Go ahead," Harry said. (This was in Carrie's hearing.)

"Can we stock her up and stay for a week or so?"

"Stay as long as you want to," Harry said. "I told you I won't be using it."

This should have been the second shock. The first, the book he was holding on his knees. After he had distributed his presents—all except the nightgown; he had simply laid that on Carrie's bed—he had taken one of the books he had got for himself out of his suitcase and made his entrance into the living room with it. He had told himself the new era must be launched at once. He had had the idea it would create its impression, him with a book. Had the idea he would not amaze them more were he suddenly to take up embroidery. As for not going to the cabin—well! In coming to his decision, he had of course imagined many difficulties that might arise out of it, but he was afraid he had not imagined no reaction. He opened his book. It was *War and Peace,* one of the ones he had cribbed a synopsis on in school. It was one of the many books that were too long for him when he was young. He cleared his throat but Carrie, whose calm he felt as a distraction, did not respond. He looked up to see that she had left the room. She had gone out to the kitchen to prepare the first meal of this home-coming. Fred was out in the hall phoning his pals. He didn't know where Ray was; maybe finding Chile on his globe? Harry felt the house tighten around him. He stared around the mahogany-heavy room. For inner permission to make for the river in the morning, he would have given a great deal. He looked down at his book:

. . . confidential maid-of-honor to the Empress Mariya Fyodorvna . . .

That name sure sounded backward to him.

4

Later—after dinner, after both boys had gone up to bed—
Harry told Carrie of his intention to take up Royall on its
offer of the job of sales manager and so come in off the road,
come home for good. No comment, no reaction. He wondered
whether she had heard. He repeated himself. No approval,
no disapproval. If there was no surprise, neither was there a
single objection. And when he finally asked her whether she
didn't think he was right in doing this, she had simply and
only said, "Yes, dear."

Looking back on it nearly twenty-four hours later—the next
afternoon—Harry was sure that this was so; that this was
what had transpired between them. The only thing was . . .
it might have been better if he had gone first to Billy Slade
and Carl and cinched the deal. Put it on ice before mention-
ing it to her. Done that and then made an announcement: "I
have taken the job as sales manager." Period. Whole thing
safely past tense and ancient history!

Now . . . He was just back from seeing Billy Slade and
Carl, with his mouth hanging open and his tongue out. Of all
the crap he had ever been handed! First Billy Slade, then
Carl. Humming and hawing around. Ants in their pants, both
of them. Change of policy! They'd been begging him to take
it every time he called in; hell, *they* had called *him*! When
had there been time for "change of policy"? It wasn't being
done in the best companies any more, recruiting future sales
managers from the ranks of their best salesmen. That was
robbing Peter to pay Paul, as the latest statistics proved.

Qualifications were different, as the latest statistics proved. And the *best* salesmen made more, when you came right down to it. Hadn't thought to inform Harry, since Harry had repeatedly turned them down, but they were getting a fellow from Grand Rapids who had practically signed on the dotted line. Now, why didn't Harry take a month off? Sure, it would be over and above his vacation which he had already racked up, but so what? Big wink. Did he think he was working for pikers? Why, he'd be fixed up with one of those little items known as a pay check to boot. Go ahead, take a month, Mike could handle his territory, get a good rest, go fishing till fish ran out of his ears, and then come back, and he'd see, there wouldn't be any holding him, he'd be rarin' to hit that old road. That was where Royall Furniture Company needed Harry, right where Royall Furniture Company had him.

And it took no highly developed sense of smell to smell the rat! The thing stank.

Brooding over it—pacing off the den—Carrie suddenly loomed up in his mind. First, it just seemed to be the humiliation of confronting her with his news that was bothering him. But almost at once he was recapitulating—remembering: he had made his intentions clear to Carrie last night. She had left the house early this morning and had not returned until around noon, shortly after which he had set out himself, to see Billy Slade and Carl. Could it be . . . ? He would have dismissed such a notion as preposterous, more than likely, had it not been fairly recently reimpressed on him—at that last company shindig—the way Carl and Billy Slade too, for all that, bent the knee to Carrie. My God, he had thought at the time, you'd think she owned Macy's. He knew old Carl pretty well, he had watched him turn it on at Market often

enough, and he knew Carl was giving Carrie the Full Treatment. When the boy of the chromium heart did that, it
meant . . .

Harry sat down heavily. She didn't own Macy's. For a
moment he lingered over that happy certainty.

After Abel's death Royall had a rough time of it for a while,
but that was nothing to what had happened ten years ago,
when Flora and Zeb died. The works were really fouled up
and Royall had changed hands twice, the second time five
years ago, and this second time (let Harry remind himself)
Carrie had had five years of playing the stock market behind
her. He reminded himself that, unlike most women, Carrie
was a gambler, she had the capacity to lose. And she also had
her reasons for being interested in Royall. Five years
ago, there were those holding Royall stock, no longer because
they wanted it but because they could not get rid of it for
anything like what they had paid for it. The market for Royall
common was thin as the devil, and on top of that, Royall
passed a dividend. So there were plenty who were trying to
work off the stock they held. Things were as shaky as hell.
Harry had thought seriously of clearing out. And it was said
around that if someone were to dump even a few thousand
shares, the price would really hit the skids. And that was
what happened. *Somebody* did dump, starting a panic, with
everybody suddenly selling; and *somebody* had bought it up
fast. Then, the sale was consummated, and the situation began to brighten. Royall was not only back where it had been
but forging ahead, Harry attributing most of the gains to the
general overhauling at the production and distribution ends
that came with more enlightened ownership and management. They were back in the black anyhow, in an amazingly

short time, and soon paying handsome dividends. Royall
common had been climbing steadily ever since.

Harry sat perfectly still. Question: how big a block of
Royall stock did Carrie own? A controlling interest? Good
God—impossible. Question: could Carrie sit on a board of
directors if she wanted to? But wouldn't she want to? Certainly, Carrie was *not* on the Royall board of directors. One
last question: *had* Carrie gone and had a little chat with
Carl? Had Harry been working for *Carrie* for—oh—five
years? He opened his hands and looked for a second at
the beads of sweat faithfully following the lines in his palms.
Holy Mary Mother of God, this could be the worst joke ever
played on a man. *Think you're working for pikers? Take a
month off, pay check to boot. Go ahead, go fishing till . . .*
and who was it who knew he had just made up his mind not
to go fishing at all?

He'd better pull up. If she did have a say-so and if she
didn't want him as sales manager, they would hardly have
offered it to him in the first place, would they? Still, he had
not challenged her then. And that quirk of hers (not allowing praise to be beamed on herself directly), she might have
approved it, like a nice, fat, juicy, extra plum being handed
her way and taking for granted, of course, that she would
manage the sales manager. No reaction? It was quite possible there was a reaction about like a ton of bricks. And if
he had been thinking that he might have to beat her at her
own game—"man to man," he thought to himself, with a curl
of the lip—it was equally possible that she had taken him in
the first round!

But hold on. The town would know, *he* would know if
Carrie virtually owned Royall or even a big slice of it. Not

even Carrie could keep a secret like that (all those damn papers he had signed). But maybe the town did know, while he was the jerk, the laughingstock who didn't; who had in fact made a special mission out of not finding out. All those rumors he hadn't listened to. Furthermore, maybe he *had* known! He was remembering some of the cracks of some of the guys out at the plant.

He could not confront Carl with his suspicions. As for confronting Carrie with them, that notion was yet more repellent to him.

And all this muddling while, wasn't he continuing to miss the main point: *that he wasn't going to travel for Royall any more?* And if they didn't want him as sales manager . . . well? He would have to quit Royall altogether? He stood up and returned to pacing the room. Sure. Simple. Go ahead—amputate. Outside of Royall, he wouldn't find one job in Peegram in which he could pull down any $15,000–$18,000 a year, or half that. So what was he going to do if he left Royall? Peddle magazine subscriptions from door to door? Very funny.

He went for a beer and came back with half of it spilled. He slammed the can down on the table (Royall's best, in the Prelude Group). You just didn't throw away a job like his unless you were planning for permanent residence in a booby hatch! He sank down into the leather chair and let his thoughts go; let them run to hell and back, for a while, on the same track. Then, suddenly, it came to him, what he would do! Why, if Royall didn't come across, he would go into business of some sort for himself. Why not? Maybe that was getting in deep, but, oddly, it was an idea that pleased him. What? No more expense account? No more Old Granddad, fruit cakes, nineteen-pound turkeys, Virginia hams, bonuses, come Christmas? No more "company benefits," in sickness and in health, till death us do part? Just where was he going to get the capital to set himself up in business? He had most of his money tied up in insurance. Well, he supposed he could borrow on it—arrange with Jesse Tate for a loan. What sort of business?

He drained his beer, rose, went out to the hall and, picking up the telephone, gave the operator the Royall number. (In Peegram, they had yet to install the dial system.) Switchboard girl—receptionist—secretary—private secretary. "Harry Hibbard here, Mary, honey. Is Mr. Lindemann around?" (Receptionists and secretaries invariably fell in love with Harry, accounting for no small part of his success as a salesman, this never having any trouble getting past the outer guard, particularly in his younger days when contacts were yet to be made. Good Lord, he thought, am I starting to reminisce?)

"Carl," he said, when Carl's voice smacked his eardrum. "Harry. Maybe I didn't make this clear. I wasn't very clear about it myself, but I've been thinking. Either I'm sales manager or Royall and I part company. O.K.?"

Carl's chromium heart did a flip or two. Oh, why, look here, Harry, old boy. Then feeding out the vacation line again, he wasn't even going to listen to Harry when what Harry needed was a rest, and all that, but not coming across with "We can't afford to lose you" or "We'll see what we can do."

When Harry could get in edgewise, he said, "No, Carl. I don't buy the vacation. You see, this means a lot to me and I've made up my mind. Unless you want to call me back within twenty-four hours to tell me I'm sales manager, we're through."

He hung up abruptly. Never had he exercised his man's privilege of talking to Carl like that! Carrie crossed the hall, just then, on her way to the kitchen, and smiled at him pleasantly.

(He had put the nightgown on her bed. He had not mentioned it and neither had she. He was waiting for her to stop behind his chair. He did not intend to go to her unless that mysterious signal went up between them.)

Watching her solid back, reviewing her smile, he wanted to laugh a wild, mad laugh that would rock the house. And was it ever given to a man—or a man his age—in these times —anything so simple as proving his manhood in bed?

5

Carl Lindemann did not call Harry back during the twenty-four hours Harry had allowed him. Harry understood that as far as Carl was concerned, he, Harry, was the one being allowed. Being allowed a tantrum, one month for recovery, and then the reconciliation. But as far as Harry was concerned, he was no longer working for Royall Furniture Company. He put this in writing, in a brief letter to Carl, and sent a copy to the accounting department with the added request that he be promptly cleared. Thus he swept his mind clean of Royall Furniture and was unable to locate any regrets even in the darkest corners.

He set about investigating business opportunities. Prowling around. Feeling his way. There ought to be something Peegram needed that Peegram did not have, something that would also be congenial from Harry's point of view. No sport-

ing goods. He drew the line there. If there was a thing dis-
tasteful to him, it was the sight of an old athlete, in a loud
plaid jacket and two-tone shoes, looking wistful behind the
counter of a sporting-goods store.

The first thing to take his fancy was the Nu-Way. This was
a locally owned supermarket on the verge of failure, for
being unable to compete with the chain store prices—the reason put forward. But as Harry went into it, it seemed to him
that the real reasons were poor management and laziness. He
was struck, for instance, by the failure to utilize local farm
products as they were in season. Also, by the very erratic system (or lack of system) of markup. Peanut butter given
away, bacon five cents higher down the line than anywhere
else in town. Only two brands of flour, but umpteen different
brands and kinds of pickles and preserves (which Peegram
folks tended to sniff at still, preferring to put up their own).
A really sorry, understocked and overpriced meat department, with a butcher contemplating most of his cows at the
bottom of his bottle (poor old Jeter, he did drink!) and an
overstocked frozen foods department, with for instance piz-
zas taking up room when not a dozen souls in Peegram could
have told you what pizza was. Harry thought there was not
a thing wrong that couldn't be made right. And the more he
looked into it, the more he liked what he saw. The location
couldn't be better—on the corner of Front and Sycamore
where parking was now no problem, but there was a big
vacant lot to the rear, which he found he could get an option
on and buy up toward the day when parking might make all
the difference. Buddy and Mac must have spent themselves
on the building itself (they had imported their architect from
Gate City), because it was a dream. Despite the present clut-

ter, the floor plan was efficient and roomy, there was plenty of storage space, the fittings and equipment were first-rate. There was Carrier air-conditioning, oil heat. Buddy and Mac in the mood to sell. Furthermore, Harry thought he knew just the man to go in with him—Charlie Volz, who had owned and managed the Big Dollar supermarket in Madison for years but who had recently sold it most successfully and was back in Peegram trying to live a life of leisure and without any liking for golf. Charlie would know all the ropes. He was fifteen years older than Harry, but they were good friends. Harry approached him. The first thing Charlie said to him was, "What does Carrie think about it?" When Harry told him he hadn't discussed it with her, Charlie ran like a deer. Harry talked himself blue in the face, but all this netted was the odd look that came into Charlie's eyes. Charlie said something to the effect that maybe the reason the Nu-Way was folding was because Carrie might already have happened to have a little money invested in "a rival firm" (Charlie was using no names) and naturally, if that were so, she'd have to see to it that her investment was protected. Why didn't Harry talk things over with Carrie first and then come back and maybe they could get together?

Harry left him.

Everywhere he turned, it was the same story. He would not have believed it. Everywhere, her name was raised like a flag. There would be that odd look at the back of their eyes which he began to be able to identify as fear.

He didn't know the ins and outs of the grocery business; he couldn't have swung it alone, even if he'd had sufficient command of the capital, which he knew he didn't. He had to drop it. There was nothing else to do.

He got interested in the idea of an insurance agency, either buying his way into one already established, or even starting one, a mutual, writing fire and liability—no life, at least not at first. Again, he needed help. What was the insurance picture in Peegram? He went to Alex Coffee, who knew insurance from the ground up, though he was no longer in it, to see what was what. Same results. *What did Carrie think about it?* Carrie was the financial wizard around here. Why, Joe Rogers had just been telling him that he would no more have opened that branch office of his without consulting Carrie than he would ship electric fans to Eskimos.

"Have you heard about Carrie's latest?" he asked.

Harry gave him no answer but sat there as if hypnotized.

"Well," Alex said, taking a tourist on a tour, "the hospital's been operating in the red ever since it opened its doors, you know, and we'd been trying to get Carrie on the board. No soap. On the whole, Carrie doesn't like being on boards. But we finally persuaded her to come in—like an expert, you know—and tell us how to get out of the hole. Sort of off the record. . . . Well, one of the first suggestions she made was that the hospital stop sending out all the sheets and linens and stuff to a commercial laundry and build its own plant. Now, as a matter of fact, this idea had occurred to us several times and we had had to drop it as being impractical, because it meant we'd offend old Sam Harbisson, whose family had endowed the hospital, in the first place, with his pappy's portrait hanging right there in the waiting room, and Sam himself owning the Model Laundry that's been doing all the hospital stuff all these years."

Alex had paused and chuckled (although what was at the

back of his eyes did not waver). "Well," he said, "Carrie showed us the way, and I declare I don't know why we didn't think of it ourselves, though it does take—how is it the French say?—finesse. Carrie made us elect old Sam to the board. Then she personally slipped the big idea into his mind and *he* came out with it, pretty as you please. Why, the hospital could save one hell of a lot of dough by doing up its own sheets, etcetera; had anybody ever thought of *that*? I declare. No hard feelings anywhere. And now old Sam's going around with philanthropy shinin' out of his eyes, and either not knowin' or not carin' that he's just lost his largest customer. I hear he's even joined Seth's church, got such a kick out of it. . . . Carrie!" Alex closed with another chuckle.

Half desperate, half facetious, Harry said, "And what about the contract for the new laundry building? Did Carrie 'show you the way' there too? Is that where she took her cut?"

Alex's eyes narrowed slightly. He nearly knocked the automobile-tire ash tray off his desk, offering Harry a cigar.

Even to think about an insurance agency, without consulting Carrie, was sheer folly and madness, Harry gathered. But the point was he could not seem to find out anything! Carrie was raised not so much like a flag as a barrier. He wasn't so anxious about the insurance idea; it didn't really excite him; he let it pass. . . . It was pretty clear, and getting clearer all the time, that Carrie didn't approach her civic and church activities as most women did, as ends in themselves. Had he ever thought of Carrie's activities as shenanigans?

Word was going the rounds that David Mull, the Ford dealer, might just be getting ready to get out. Dave was in his sixties and, like Jeter the butcher, he had been hitting the bottle pretty hard now for several years. Dave, as everybody said, wasn't what he used to be. Pressure was being brought to bear on him, whether from on high or locally, either nobody knew or those who did know were not divulging. Harry got more than a little excited over the possibilities of landing the Ford agency. He knew cars and he liked them. He would like selling them. In Peegram, Ford was a winner. Virgie Fox, who was Dave Mull's general factotum, informed Harry that Dave was out of town, away on a fishing trip in Canada, and could not be reached. (This was another way of saying Dave was again at Keeley Institute, taking the cure.) He said Dave ought to be back in a couple of weeks. Harry had told Virgie nothing of his real reasons for wanting to get hold of Dave, but in a little town where there are no secrets and where not only the fact that Harry was trying to go into business for himself but also every move that he made was promptly recorded on the tape recorder of the town's consciousness, Harry was not too taken aback when Virgie slyly indicated he was onto Harry. However, he was badly taken aback when Virgie went on to say that if a certain party was so interested in a Ford agency, he might just want to bear it in mind that there was somebody other than Dave Mull to sound out, since somebody had been keeping Dave afloat, so to speak, with a bit of money as ballast, so to speak, and that naturally this somebody would have a say in the agency's future. Virgie wasn't saying who this somebody was—maybe "one of the big Baptists"—looking off over Harry's head. As he left, Harry was saying to himself, "Steady, Harry. Steady on, now. Steady, boy."

There were other ideas, other collapses of ideas. Peegram horizons were not infinite.

6

He went to see Jesse Tate at the bank. Jesse sent for Cokes, took Harry into his office and closed the door. God knew, Harry wished he could say he had come for a loan, but a loan *for what?* He sat with his head ducked a little, pinching up the skin of his forehead, of his eyelids. Jesse sat quiet, looking out the window. Neither one had touched his Coke. Time came when you had to cut across your fear of playing the fool for the sake of getting at the truth. Jess would know he had broken with Royall; he would have heard of Harry's maneuvers. His silence spoke for all this and more.

"Jess . . ."

"What is it, son?"

"Carrie's a very rich woman." (Not quite statement, not quite question.)

"You could say so, by Peegram standards," Jesse said, but immediately adding, "by any standards at all, I reckon."

Harry shifted his weight. "I know this is going to sound funny as hell, Jess, coming from me, but . . . does Carrie own a controlling interest in Royall Furniture Company?"

The question hung fire between them. Harry was aware that Jesse's perfect retort was, "Why don't you ask her?" But he had too much understanding and quick sympathy to give it back to Harry like that. He did not even show surprise over such manifest stupidity and ignorance on the part of the man who should have known first of all. Neither did he say he could not violate the confidence of a client. After a longish pause, he said, "If it's not controlling, she's certainly a very substantial stockholder. That's about all I can say about that, son."

Harry stared at him. "You wouldn't say she's also got a finger in every goddamn pie in this town?"

Jesse coughed, but it was not the kind of a cough that is held behind the hand. He looked thoughtful, his eyes crinkling in his face that was every bit as tender and creased and scuffed and as much itself in its complete inability to be other than itself as an old shoe. It occurred to Harry—he supposed it was why he had come to him—that there was no fear hiding out in Jesse's eyes.

Jesse said, "It's too bad there isn't more diversified industry around here—I've always held as much, though there are plenty of folks who wouldn't agree with me, Harry. Peegram *is* a kind of closed town, depending as it does on the Royall payroll. I guess you could almost say that the one who controls Royall controls Peegram, or is anyway in a position to." He reached for his Coke. "I'm thinking of Abel."

Harry nodded; he felt calmer.

"Abel was a real cuss," Jesse said. "By the Lord, Abel ran everything around here and everybody knew it. You knew where you stood with him. Nothing secret about it. Step on *his* toes and you got knocked galley-west. You couldn't sneeze lest Abel said you could. You couldn't have hemorrhoids lest Abel approved. Oh, Abel roared around like a lion, Harry. Yet Abel wasn't so bad. And he kept this little old town humming, Abel did. He did a lot for the town."

"Yes," Harry said, "he did."

"Carrie, now . . ." Jesse looked deep into his Coke. "Well, Carrie's got Abel's genius—we might as well face that—but she's different."

"She doesn't roar," Harry said at once.

Jesse laughed. "That's right. Step on her toes and the only thing is, you may find that your own shoes all of a sudden seem to be fittin' too tight, pinchin' a mite—you don't get slammed around, you aren't even sure what happened. Carrie knows already what size shoes you wear and where you bought them and the exact location of all your corns, which sort of knowledge old Abel would have considered a clutterment to his mind, for all his permitting you to have or not to have your hemorrhoids. What I'm trying to say is, Abel was no politician. Carrie is. And if Abel didn't have it, that's still an Erwin trait she's come by honest enough. Royall was Abel's baby, whereas Carrie is in politics, Harry. Politics is her meat. Scheming. Working folks. And it's specially interesting, because she's got no use in this world for titles and honors and all such as that that most of us fall for. Oh, she'll work hard to get into the position to have a say in handing them out, and she'll invent new ones too for others, but for herself she wouldn't count a peck of them worth the paper they're written on. 'Give all the glory to the fools,' seems to be her motto. So what does she want? Yes, Harry, the town would like to know, don't you feel so alone! Working behind the scenes—she always works behind the scenes. Staying invisible. Nobody ever knowing quite what she's about. She's a politician that never runs for office, so how can you kick her out? There's no way to get her out—you can't even say she's got a machine."

Jesse stopped for breath. Harry lighted a cigarette.

Jesse said, "With her, it's not 'divide and conquer.' It's dispensing those honors and titles and rewards we were talking about, but it's more than that, it's salting you down for future reference by keeping in mind what sort of favor you are apt to need, or appreciate most, and then when you are lowest, doing you that favor, which also happens to be the sort of favor you'll have to do something about in return, if and when. 'If and when' looms big. Nothing so simple as being nice to folks when they're sick, though she doesn't forget that. She'll toss a contract your way when business is bad, she'll lend you five hundred dollars toward your down payment on a house. And you always wonder how in the hell she knew. And of course you come to realize she can do the opposite too. She's the one onto you, and she's the one who can *not* throw that contract your way. . . . Without vanity, Harry, it seems as if that's what she plays on most—vanity—and, I do think, male vanity at that."

Harry pulled on his cigarette.

"Energy around the clock. If running Peegram is what she's after, she's darn near accomplished it, for weaving practically everybody into her cloth. She can break more people around here than we'd probably care to believe. I don't mean to imply she goes around breaking them up like sticks or kindling—there's nothing mean or petty about Carrie—but she's able to."

"She's Abel too," was the way Harry's mind translated these last words.

"Being able to—maybe it's that that's so important to her down to the minutest details—I don't know. But with that elephant's memory of hers, I don't think she *can* forget anything. Guess it makes us all uneasy. Lots of fellows her same age would give a lot for the chance to go back to the sixth grade and do that part of it over."

Harry thought of Seth, whose shame for Carrie, that night

of the senior dance, had made him want to hit him. But now, instead of wanting to hit him, he found himself thinking, "Poor Seth." Thinking this was a very odd conversation for him to be having with Jesse; thinking you could not call it anything other than collusion.

"So, yes, Harry," Jesse was saying, "she's got a finger in all the pies, maybe. But under cover. Without roaring, like we said, or letting *anybody* in on what it means. The security of Abel, that safeness you feel around *knowing,* seems a long way away. And I've got the notion it's the invisible Carrie who's got the town so nervous and buffaloed. Take Mayor Franklin. He's Carrie's boy, though I'm not sure he knows he is, just sort of suspects. Carrie wants this done or that done and he does it, thinking he thought of it himself—Carrie playing to that, of course—making him out the big shot. She goes her way so quiet and she doesn't seem to know how to deviate. You ever see her walk fast or slow? No. Nobody ever has."

Harry found himself remembering the night a tramp came knocking at their back door. Carrie had sat him down and cooked him a big meal and got him a room at the hotel and put a twenty-dollar bill into his hand as he was leaving and told him to call her in the morning so they could see what they could do about a job (and she got him a job too, street cleaning, if Harry remembered correctly). "And who was that?" he had asked her afterward, "the Prince of Wales?" Carrie had seemed so surprised that Harry hadn't recognized him. That was Tom Sparks from out in the county they had been in grammar school with. Maybe Tom Sparks had looked at Carrie without being repelled, long ago; picked up a handkerchief for her or held a door. Or maybe he was just being "salted down" toward the future, as a vote, as a man neither too lowly nor too far gone to be used. He could see he was no politician. And he was beginning to see that being the popular favorite, the hero, even the old hero, was very different from being whatever Carrie was.

Jesse was saying, "Not her. You won't catch her putting all her eggs in one basket. And the folks who thought that when she got her hands on Royall she would rest content were just as wrong as they could be. Who knows what the limit is? We don't have the full picture. Neither does D&B nor the Federal Government, I would bet. (Carrie knows that Income Tax Manual better than a lot of lawyers around here do, and if you catch her brooding over something, it's apt to be the fine print!) No, Carrie's not having anybody know too much about her. She banks here, sure, but she banks at Madison and other places as well. She wouldn't have *me* know too much about her."

"Or me," Harry thought. He got up, saying, "I'm only married to her." The joke Jesse eagerly accepted. Their collusion brushed, but brushed lightly, with shame.

"Well, Jess, I . . ."

". . . anything I can do for you, Harry, you know I'll be glad to."

"Yeah, well, I . . . I'll hope to be coming in soon to touch you for a loan."

"Good. Wish there was something I could put you onto. If I hear of something, I'll . . ."

"Sure."

They shook hands.

Arriving home, he had an idea that rocked him. What Peegram needed that it did not have was a store for kids, starting with babies and moving right on up through the teens. Toys. Rattles and teethers and teddy bears. Little silver spoons and cups and such. Bootees! Those little old dresses that you couldn't find for the lace. Gift wrapping a specialty, pink and blue. Diapers by the dozen. Those little ditty shirts. Safety pins, plain and in colors. Santa Claus at Christmas, handing out lollypops. Good line for teen-agers. Nothing so fancy as to scare off Royall workers. Call it The Young Ages or The Land of Lilliput or Stop and Shop for the Young Ones or something.

This was a hot idea. Over his third beer, it was an extremely hot idea. What they could call it was Carrie's Husband's Folly or The Old Athlete's Retreat. And they could laugh themselves into a coma about it. But it *wasn't* a bad idea, by God. He had heard Elaine and other ladies complain many a time for having to drive all the way to Madison for kid stuff. . . . Rather needed a woman in the picture, though. Help with the buying. He'd sure go wrong on those little old dresses. As for the diaper demand, he was afraid he could not estimate it. Ask Carrie to put all her eggs in this basket with him?

. . . A motel, maybe. Peegram was on a main route to the mountains. He would look into that.

Didn't need another beer to know he was making a complete fool of himself—without opening Carrie's Husband's Folly. He knew. He also knew that all eyes were on him—all those eyes, with the fear playing hide and seek at the back of them. *We won't help you, we can't help you. But can you? Will you?* He *was* their (secret) hero. Odd, being so trapped. Nor could he seem to get back the perspective of the road.

Well, he would look into the motel idea right away. And

he sat down and wrote Pete McCloud, an old fraternity brother of his who now managed the Western Auto store in Gate City. He knew there were Western Auto stores in both Stoneville and Lower Creek, both much smaller and poorer towns than Peegram. He asked Pete a lot of questions, asked for names of the men he ought to contact and so on. He would have called Pete long distance except he was afraid it might seem too desperate. For the same reason, he did not send the letter special delivery. Nothing succeeds like success, he reminded himself.

7

Meanwhile, between his increasingly wretched sorties on the town (the motel idea did not work out; he had not yet heard from Pete who was perhaps away on vacation), Harry tried to keep himself occupied around the house. But no faucets dripped. Hinges weren't off. Nothing needed oiling. A colored man took care of the lawn with a power mower. The attic (stifling hot) was as neat as a pin; there were not even any boxes to rummage in. Maybe he had seen himself mending the electric fan over a long conversation with Ray? A fan belonging to Carrie would not have the temerity to drop a screw, much less break down. As for Ray, Harry could not seem to find him. He was almost never around except at meal times. Ray seemed to live his life according to what Harry caught himself thinking of as Carrie's law. He lived it outside the house, in the environs of back yard and neighborhood, and beyond Harry's reach. Unless it rained, apparently, Ray did not play in the house, and it had not rained. When Ray was the one who had really brought him home, when Ray was the one whose need for salvation had pressed most on him, it seemed especially disquieting. If Harry tried to coax him in and read to him, or play some of the records he had brought, Ray became ill at ease, almost frightened, almost as if he thought he was being made to run the gauntlet for his father's sake. This reversal—because Harry, surely, was the one running the gauntlet—seemed so strange! And more than strange—even terrifying!—that *Arabian Nights* could be a punishment rather than the pleasure the boy was by nature so conditioned to revel in. But . . . "Where's Carrie?" he would want to know. (Except when addressing her directly, he called her Carrie too.) And he could not concentrate, because he could not disobey Carrie's law, which said he played outside in the summer except when it rained, without trembling. By God, Harry thought, if I didn't know different, I'd think she beat him. *She's destroyed him* already. And now what? Patience, he warned himself. If Ray's salvation could be achieved in a day, he would not stand in such need of it. ("Cherish me, Daddy." "Yes, my son.") It was as well that Fred was not around. He could not have endured that teetering back on his heels now. . . .

Harry read, read *War and Peace*, picked it up and put it down between sorties on the town. Jumped whenever the phone rang, though it did not ring for him. When she was talking over the phone, he would hear her mention his name, quite often, and always with the utmost respect, but always, as he began to take in, as though he were not present, not there. He realized she was bragging on his prowess as a fisherman. And while, at first, he had been too involved in town trying to put himself in business to notice it, he began to see, as time hung more and more heavily upon him, that something very queer was going on in their home; something advancing their quarrel that had to advance without words. With a nightgown laid on a bed. And then:

He noticed that, at table, a place was set for him only at nights. This was no accident, it was s.o.p., standard operational procedure, as he discovered. Mornings and noons, he would come in, take a look, give that laugh that was getting familiar, say, "Forgot me, huh?" and go out to the kitchen, collect a plate and hardware and bring them to the table himself. Noons, the menus were conspicuously made up of what he did not like—cucumber salads, soufflés and such; nights, his specialties regularly appeared, French fries and steaks, hush puppies and fish (from the deep-freeze box). What did Ray think, coming to the table where only two places were set, one for her and one for him and none for the father trying to laugh it off? Whatever he thought, Ray was most attentive. Mornings and noons, she did not speak to Harry unless he spoke first. Nights, she was affable and polite; making conversation in which she presented him with his own opinions.

He noticed that only the evening paper, the Madison *Observer,* was kept sacred to his touch.

He noticed that beer was not apt to appear in the refrigerator, at least not where he could find it, until late afternoons.

He noticed that regularly, every evening at six o'clock on the dot, she would stop whatever she was doing (and if she were out, she would return home at this hour) and go up to his room and lay out a complete change of clothes on his bed, this change invariably including slacks and sports shirt. And since he was doing his changing, his showering and his shaving in the mornings, these days, and since in view of his sorties on the town wearing suits instead of slacks and sports shirts, this seemed particularly mystifying and annoying. Every night, before getting into bed, he would have to throw the clothes over a chair where, after the light was off and the darkness had settled (he was not sleeping well), they would begin to take on odd, ghost-like shapes upon which he would find himself fixing his strained attention.

Then one morning, if it could be said that he had slept at all, he woke up at his old river-going hour, four o'clock, that hour when he would have thrown on his clothes, made his own breakfast, grabbed the lunch Carrie would have fixed for him the night before (his gear would already be in the car), and bolted. He wandered downstairs and on out to the kitchen where he turned on the light. There—on the stove—in ghostly greeting to a ghost, yet more profoundly shocking for its reality as that reality was framed by the unreal—were strips of bacon in the frying pan, eggs set out in a white crockery bowl, his thermos, his lunch box on the counter alongside. Silex loaded, coffee topside, water in the bottom. In a trance, with all the formality of the ballet dancer who knows full well what is expected of him next, he turned and opened the refrigerator door. In a tall glass, his orange juice. Wrapped in waxed paper, his sandwiches, his pickles, his cookies poised for his own completing of the ritual. Which was, placing them in the lunch box. Softly, he closed the refrigerator door. Literally, with the back of his hand, he wiped the smile from off his face.

He went out to the back porch and sat down on the

steps. The sky was pearling in the east, the sleepy birds just beginning to wake. (And the fish—from the deep freeze —to remind him; he did not care for them half so much when they were not water fresh.)

Terms. As a fisherman he was not to be excelled. The Royall job, the salesman's job, was waiting for him too. It is preferable to forget that somebody has been making a great fool of himself. Co-operate and consider forthwith that forgetting accomplished, the myth of manhood maintained, inasmuch as none of this has ever been and no one laid a nightgown, with a lot of lace on it, in the biggest size made, upon a bed. And no one went poaching on another's preserves. Terms. Business as usual. Yes?

A kindness, a generosity about it too. As the old hero in hiding he was a valuable asset. She could always use him as window-dressing. *She closed the window . . . !* Now, he supposed, his crazy dream mind would set to work punning on that too—punning was the lowest form of wit—so that he would begin to see her dressing at the window in the nightgown with all the lace on it.

Couldn't he knuckle under? Behave himself? Be as he had been? He would be meticulously rewarded. Couldn't he see it was the only way?

Suddenly he laughed out. He would hand it to her: she was most exquisitely insulting! Behold the woman who had once fought him like a fiend (before giving in).

Royall salesman, fisherman, hunter and former athlete, couldn't he understand how virile he was (on the former schedule of his comings and goings), which was all that the civilized future could be built on. She had learned that to defeat the male, you simply do not provide him with an adversary. You do not give him the chance to fight.

It was not overconfidence (and she would never use words) that made her present her terms. So how should he reply? Divorce? Clearing out for good? Stop poaching on her preserves and leave Peegram, taking with him only the younger boy? No, not yet, though he must note that he was thinking of this. She had been forging her armor these years that he had been running away. Forging armor or spooning out slow poison—which? Perhaps it was not so much herself she had strengthened as others that she had weakened.

Theirs was an essentially private battle still, even if the town was in it in a triangular arrangement—never the *two*, in this world, but always the everlasting *three*. . . . If they should ever get it straight between them, would he care that he had a rich wife? Of course not! He would be able to ask her, in the easiest way, to help him establish The Land of Lilliput or anything else. And so that they brought their hearts home again, who should judge how sad or how destroying an answer she had found it necessary to give, for a while, to Abel and Flora and Zeb, and Seth, and to the town that had hurt her. That had named her, by its standards, a freak. No. He would not have cared, even as the dense center of all this was his own unmanning, knowing that curious sympathy for her, when she was so smart and so strong; and when she didn't have it and he did.

The pearling sky was bleeding at the seams, but it was a phenomenon of sheer beauty. He would not accept her terms.

Later that same day—at breakfast, in fact; when Ray was also at the table—he said quietly to her that unless he should inform her that he was going out, he would expect a place set for him at every meal thereafter. She said, "Of course, dear," and as if she had of course been doing it right along.

After that there was always a place punctiliously set— *too* "set," with extra trimmings, like a linen napkin when theirs were paper ones, and as if he were a guest. The menus became, if anything, a trifle more conspicuous than before, and the clothes continued to be ritualistically laid out on his bed, and (as he knew, without again venturing down to the kitchen to see) each morning all was in readiness for his capitulation, for his return to the river. . . . Playing him, waiting now to see him turn over and show his belly. But put very simply, he refused her terms.

8

Peegram horizons were not infinite. Till now it had never really been brought home to him how important a job, or being in business, or making money was to a man's self-esteem. He continued his search, yet time hung ever more heavily upon him, when there was nothing *to do*. He understood that he was not holding his own. He understood that *something* had to happen. Nor was it going "to happen" unless he engineered it. He tried a person-to-person call to Pete McCloud and discovered he was away but would be back in a few days. Disproportionately, as he feared, he pinned his hopes on Pete.

And, meanwhile, he would not admit he had moved out

of the house (that home he was going to save) and into the
back yard. One could still hear the phone ring from out there.
Maggie, the bird-dog bitch, was out there in her pen—he
liked looking at her. And there was a string hammock out
there, slung between the walnut and the sycamore, a good
spot to read.

This afternoon, he was lying in the hammock, with his
book open on his abdomen, watching the clouds, brooding,
and absently registering the kids' shouts. The kids—Ray and
his friends—were playing *catch-a-fly-you're-up* in the next
lot on which no house stood, since Harry had bought the
two lots together when they had decided to build. It was a
pie-shaped corner lot that had turned into the neighborhood playground after the blight had taken the mimosa
trees which were its chief planting and which Carrie had
had cleared. Lying there, Harry was vaguely wishing he
was the sort of old hero who could barge in on the kids'
game, in the belief he was doing them a favor, when—suddenly—there was a loud crash and the sound of breaking
glass.

He sat up. A baseball had gone through the living-room
window, the big window that was not screened. Harry
noted that the children neither cried out nor scattered but
came on over into the yard and drew close together—in
silence. He noted that they were entirely unaware of his
existence and had the distinct impression that if he reminded
them of it, they would resent it as being extraneous.

"She won't ask who done it," one of the boys said.

Silence. Ray did not seem to have anything to contribute
to this. He stood smaller and punier than the others, that
was all. In no way did he seem to stand out as the son who

might be counted upon to save the situation. If anything, they would save him, it would seem, since they rather pushed him to their rear.

Carrie came out on the porch, solid and unsmiling, with the ball making a conspicuous bulge in her apron pocket. She looked the children over. Like a general, Harry thought, reviewing troops. Cool, when everybody else was hot. At ease, when all the rest were ramrods. Taking her time.

Seth's boy, William Morrison, was the one who finally spoke up.

"Carrie," he said. "We'll take up a collection out of our allowances. You call up the store and find out how much it costs. Did we break anything besides the window?"

"A vase," Carrie said.

"Expensive?" William Morrison wanted to know.

"Gift," Carrie said.

The children said, "Oh."

"This time," Carrie said, "I will pay for the window. If there's a next time, you will."

They nodded gravely. Then they shuffled around, re-organizing their ranks. Carrie waited. William Morrison, in a formal way, told her they wouldn't be needing any lemonade and cookies this afternoon. Whereupon Carrie took the ball out of her pocket and dropped it. All of them watched, fascinated, while it rolled slowly across the grass. When it came to a full stop, Carrie turned and went inside.

Harry lay back. He heard William Morrison say, "There ain't going to be no next time." Harry felt that William Morrison was absolutely right! He lay there, abdomen rising and falling under the book. Not just Seth's boy, all the children called her Carrie rather than Mrs. Hibbard.

Was it her custom to serve them lemonade and cookies? What were they to her? Were even they—kids—grist for her mill? Or was it done like baby-kissing, with one eye on the parents and as an investment in "good will"? The scene had chilled him. But actually she had handled it extremely well. Fairly and without any fuss. Nor had she tried to scrimp their natures, the way so many women did. Furthermore, it was damned impressive, the whatever-it-was that was so completely understood between them. There had never been any question of disobedience, only of error. They had voluntarily taken punishment on themselves. Carrie was certainly not the one who had suggested it. This geography of Carrie—maybe the kids were the only ones who had it figured. It was a healthy sort of fear they entertained for her, a fear not unmixed with affection (obviously they held her in high regard), and as if taking it completely for granted, her power over them. Yes, adults might not know where they stood with Carrie, complaining that she was invisible, but the children knew exactly and did not question it any more than rain. Which might be all very well if you weren't a part of the geography yourself. One little boy . . . One little boy had not cried out to the man in the hammock for help. That little boy also knew where he stood. Of course, he hadn't been the one to speak up. It was William Morrison, Seth's boy, who had done the talking.

After supper of that same day Harry interrupted the game of Red Light that the kids were playing in the vacant lot and took Ray with him for a walk. Ray did not object inasmuch as he had half an hour before he had to be in the house. Darkness was coming on and the new moon was holding the old moon in its arms, as the saying goes. They took "the street the Brittains lived on." The air was heavy and close, as if it were no less and no more than a saturated solution of the river. One lone cicada's wail rose, throbbed, and held the throbbing until it became unbearable, before it fell off into the darkness that smothered it at last. Harry described the phases of the moon to Ray. "Then there is the full of the moon," he said, but remembering privately, and possibly because the river was all around him, that bass —big-eyed game fish—will not rise to a line in the full of the moon; they will feed through the moonlight night and will not rise to any line the next day. Moon, wind, water and "the sign." Out on the river itself the air would not be this close; the faintest breeze would be freshening over the water.

They walked on in the silence that Harry's words had left in their wake. But instead of saying "Cherish me, Daddy," Ray reached for his father's hand and held it close. As for the moon . . . well, it was the new moon which was holding the old moon in its arms.

9

His desire to meet her terms was almost more than he could endure. His nights, beginning to be disturbed by strange dreams in which he was always fishing or hunting. He had begun to dread the nights more acutely than the days.

It had got so he was trying frantically to reach Pete McCloud, long distance, even though he knew Pete could not be back yet. He was waiting between mail delivery and mail delivery, while he knew there was nothing to wait for.

He could hardly bear to look at Carrie now. Partly, it was his own sense of failure that forbade him, but more, it was that he had begun to see her as monstrous, as disfigured by disease, by the terrible tumorous cancer of sterility growing in her (the fertility of sterility, he would think), which he could not stop, no more than the best surgeon with all his skills could have, when it was too late; when, to cut it out one place was only to find it again in another. The rapidly growing morbid cells. Death could grow as fast as life could. Faster.

At the present pass, there was as far as he could see only one stone that he had left unturned—real estate—and it was maybe curious that he should have avoided it when it was the business his father had been in. But to him land was somehow not a commodity. He would go bankrupt from stalling around, insisting that the land suit the man and the man the land. He loved land too much and would never be a bit good trying to extract a profit out of it. Now, he owned a fine tract that his father had left him and never had been willing to sell a foot of it, though he had had plenty of offers, the Lord knew.

So what was he going to do? It seemed to him that without his being aware of it, the emphasis had shifted: that it was no longer *what* he was going to do that loomed so big. Something else came first, something having to do with the banishing of false pride, something having to do with his response to her presenting of terms—take them or leave them, boy—these terms of the generous conqueror. As if it were now incumbent upon him to so work it that he, with

poise and dignity, should be able to reply by the simple
request for her help. *His* terms. The Ford agency would be
best. But how, in what way, he was to achieve this he
could not imagine. They did have to get into the arena first,
he knew that. He knew she should not be allowed to proclaim herself conqueror for locking the gates of the arena
tight. Plainly, he no longer knew where in the hell that
arena was, much less where the keys to the gates could be
concealed. And that he could not ask her to help him now,
without losing his soul, he knew absolutely.

He was lying in the hammock, thinking all this—watching
the clouds (he had reached page 259 of *War and Peace*)—
when he saw Jim coming around the corner of the house,
walking slowly, with his head bent.

He was on his feet at once. "Hello, Jim!" he called. "Here
I am!" Across the yard in a trice. Feeling almost as if he had
been granted a reprieve. "Lord, it's good to see you, Jim."
Shaking hands, sitting down together on the steps, Jim
grunting. They never had talked much.

"Where's Jimbo?" Harry asked.

"Oh," Jim said vaguely, "around."

Harry thought that Jim seemed depressed and more than
usually shut up inside himself. They took out cigarettes,
each his own, and smoked in silence. Jim brought the river
to the back door. He was the only other man Harry knew
with whom he was deeply willing to share it. Oh, he could
go fishing with Fred and enjoy it, but it was not the same
as fishing with Jim. He was always conscious that he was
"teaching" Fred; that while Fred was a sportsman, he was
not a philosopher, so that fishing with him meant the bottom
level of meaning was missing. Fred was the one to go hunt-

ing with—he would stay with you longer than you could hold out, walking your legs off, and he was superb with dogs—but for fishing it was Jim and it always had been since they were knee-high, playing hooky by prearrangement, meeting each other where the paths forked in the pinewoods, each with his cane pole and his can of worms. The down-log where whoever got there first sat waiting for the other. It was Jim who had first shown Harry how to stick a worm through the rooter. And it was Jim, not Harry, who had first got hold of a boat. They were stern and generous toward each other, yet secretly competitive. Harry had to acknowledge Jim's wrist was the better one. To each the other was the only fishing companion possible, which went without saying, though there were those long stretches, never discussed and never explained, when each had to do his fishing alone.

Jim was light-skinned, heavy-set, and so strongly resembled Zeb Erwin that nobody, except Seth, had any doubts about his paternity. (Seth didn't so much doubt it as he was struck blind by it, Harry suspected.) Jim was a careful, controlled, formal sort, verging on pompous when he didn't have his fishing rod about him. And while he was so efficient that he kept a good job (he was head janitor at the high school), he nevertheless inspired white people's dislike and mistrust. The high-school paper had never done any folksy little feature, with photo, on Jim, though it had near immortalized Cindy, the cafeteria cook. Harry was sure Jim knew none of the high-school students by name and he could imagine that if any of them said "Hi-ya, Jim" to him, while he was about his business with the pushbroom, all they would get from him would be a frigid nod. Jim did not address white people as "Mr. Harry" or "Miss Carrie," the way the other Peegram Negroes did. When he called Harry anything, which was seldom and never during their boyhood, it was "sir," this dating from Army days when Jim was a sergeant and Harry a commissioned officer and which, while their paths had not crossed during the war, allowed Jim, at last, some form of address.

Jim's formal education had stopped in the seventh grade when he had to start supporting his mother, flat on her back with paresis by that time, and the small fry in that fatherless family; Jim was the oldest. Harry had heard that he took books out of the high-school library, *The Decline and Fall of the Roman Empire* and such, according to the librarian, with whom he had not, however, come to any beautiful understanding inasmuch as he did not consult her (did not even check the books out properly, but took and returned them, on his own, in secret, all before or after hours), so that she had long since ceased to think of it as cute.

Harry had heard it around that Jim belonged to the NAACP and attended meetings in Madison; he had heard that at heart Jim was an agitator and a radical who did not know his "place." But he knew nothing about any of this firsthand and did not care to. His and Jim's friendship was strictly around fishing. He had seen the look deep in Jim's eyes but also knew, with a kind of wondering gratitude, that it did not apply to him.

Harry made no bones about Jim's paternity. He thought it was a damn shame. If Old Zeb hadn't been able to control himself any better than that, he might still have done better by his son. At least enabled him to complete his education. No, Harry was not at all oblivious of Jim's kin to Carrie and Seth. He was Carrie's first cousin, as much as Seth was, and Seth's half-brother, so why pussyfoot around about it? Indeed, he knew that he, being plain Hibbard, perfectly good third-generation Erwin County Hibbard, though ungiven to the sowing of bastards, took his measure of satisfaction in maintaining relations with the one whose existence the lordly Erwins, in all politeness, saw no reason to acknowledge. When Carrie met up with Jim anywhere, she gave him the casual greeting she gave to all the Negroes she knew and called by their first names, and moved on at that steady pace of hers. Never a ripple. And if Jim should draw a switch-blade on her in an alley, she would not recognize him, not even to stay the knife, not even in her last gasp. Harry had decided it must also afford Jim a certain, perhaps painful, satisfaction, this being friends with the husband of his white cousin who was not driven to being (even secretly) rude to him.

This friendship of theirs had never aroused any undue comment since it was around fishing. It was accepted readily enough, there was plenty of precedent for it, it was permitted. The general knowledge concerning Jim's paternity made no difference one way or the other. Nearly everybody except Harry did pussyfoot, did "forget" it out of courtesy to the Erwins, though Harry had the feeling they could "remember" it again, on occasion, in a hurry, and enjoyed this "remembering" thoroughly. After all, every town must have its quota of idiots and bastards and scandal for the sake of glamour. Many a time, in front of the high school, Harry would sit in his car, waiting for Jim to get through with his pushbroom. "Going fishing again, I see," was the standard comment of acquaintances happening past. Then they would swing around by Jim's house to pick up his tackle and gear. Perfectly aboveboard, since Harry never went in. They did ride together in the front seat, but that was all right. Indeed, except that they took turns providing lunch—ham biscuits, when it was Jim's turn —there was nothing amiss in their relationship.

Last Christmas, Harry had given Jim an expensive rod and reel. He had worried about it, and it was one of the happiest moments of his life when it turned out to be a gift Jim could accept. Jim gave Harry a pair of hand-knitted gloves. Since Jim's wife was not in the picture (Harry didn't know what happened to her; he had never heard and never asked), he thought Jim must have knitted the gloves himself. They were exactly the right size.

Jimbo was all Jim had in the world, the legacy left to him by his never-mentioned wife. Jimbo was a year or two younger than Ray. Jim was both father and mother to him, and, in the light of his own troubles, Harry suspected that he verged on being envious of the closeness between them. He would catch himself watching intently, the way Jim would yank Jimbo's sweater down, or set his cap straight on his head, or hold a handkerchief to his nose, or slap him. Often they took Jimbo with them as far as the landing, where he would install himself, stubby black legs dangling over the side, with his pole and his can of worms, and his own quota of ham biscuits distributed among his pockets. No matter how late they stayed out, Jim never worried about Jimbo. (Harry would not dare leave Ray alone on the landing for five minutes!) Many a time they came back to find him curled up like a puppy on the cabin porch, fast asleep,

with maybe one very dead little catfish by his side, and
biscuit crumbs all over his mouth, to tell of his day's work.

"Pickaninny," Harry had heard Jim say once, under his
breath, as he was lifting Jimbo up to carry him out to the
car where he would not deposit him on the back seat, but
hold him cradled, the whole way back to town. Jim could
"pass" for white; Jimbo was as black as a domino. That
night Harry thought he had a clue as to why Jim, who
would not lick the boots of any white man, let his son be
called Jimbo, which had that unmistakable Sambo connotation, though it was also a contraction of "Jim boy"—maybe
he wanted the little black bugger to learn young that in a
world of discrimination and insult, the language of insult
could also be the language of love.

Harry stirred and flipped his cigarette across the grass;
Jim sent his after it. Ever secretly competitive, Harry
thought with a smile, mine won by a good three inches.

"How's the river?" he asked abruptly, if guardedly. "I
. . . haven't been out there since I got back. Guess you've
heard I've been busy."

"Don't know," Jim said.

Harry said, "*What?*"

"Haven't been out myself."

It was a long, strained, pregnant pause. Harry shifted his
weight.

"Been too worried about the house," Jim said. "Had too
much on my mind for fishing."

Harry waited. Was it true that misery loves company? He
felt unusually close to Jim. What about his house? Jim was
proud of his house, kept it painted a gleaming white, and
a few years back, had built a picket fence around it. It was

an old house (under the paint), in one of those fringe areas, not quite in the colored section proper, and marred by Highway 70, which ran directly behind it, with the big trucks shifting gears on the hill. When the picket fence appeared, it had made a lot of white folks who thought Jim was uppity anyhow angry to look at it. And it made them angry too, that Jim had a lawn that he mowed rather than beaten-down dirt and weeds, with a hen or two scratching.

"Mayor Franklin is selling the house," Jim said.

"I thought you owned it," Harry said.

"No, he never would sell to me, though I've kept it up, put in the fence and all. I've been renting it for nine years. But Mr. Franklin is selling the site to somebody who plans to put up a filling station on it."

Harry said nothing; he knew how Jim felt about the house. And, damn it, it wasn't right!

"They're tearing down the house," Jim said in his perfectly flat voice. "I looked into the possibilities of buying it myself and having it moved. But there aren't any vacant lots anywhere around there other than the old Kirksey one, which is over the line, of course—in the white neighborhood. Then they tell me the house is too old and rotten to move anyhow, it would fall down."

"I guess so," Harry said.

"I've been combing the town. . . . I can't find one decent place to move to."

Harry nodded. "I'll bet. It gets my blood up, every time I drive down Mimosa Avenue."

Jim looked over at him. "Mimosa Avenue? Why, that's Fifth Avenue, sir. That's class. Mr. Franklin has made his fortune on rentals extracted from the colored population.

He doesn't have to put in any improvements, he knows we have no place to move, and he charges just as much rent as the traffic will bear. Most streets—it isn't just that they aren't paved. Half of them, there's no garbage collection, no . . . But you've seen the privies."

"My God," Harry muttered. "I thought the City Council—"

"—put in a few fire hydrants? Yes. So Mr. Franklin could get the insurance rates he wanted."

Jim laughed. In the wake of that laugh, they both lighted fresh cigarettes.

"I'm not having the boy grow up in a sty," Jim said. "I'm not having him associating with swine and drunkards. But I can't find even a half-decent place—I can't even find a lot to put up a shack on (I've a little money saved). We've got to be out of the house in another two weeks. We were given one month's notice."

Harry was thinking, his thoughts revolving around one central idea: he owned land, didn't he? Several hundred acres of it. He had leased timber rights (selective cutting) on some of it, but that was all. It was all his. . . . Why not?

"I own some land, Jim." He turned quickly toward Jim, turned away as quickly. "All that land around the cabin, up and down, is mine," he said. He understood the power of saying one had fathered the most beautiful virgin anywhere; he could feel Jim's suppressed excitement. "I haven't wanted just everybody sharing that old river with me," he went on. "But I can't think of a thing wrong with lopping you off a piece of that land that looks right over it." To think that problems could be solved like this!

Harry said, "I'd be proud to make you a present of a bit of land, Jim. Then, maybe, you could take that money you have socked away and build a house. You could do a lot of it yourself. Remember the cabin?" Jim had helped Harry build the cabin. Between them, they had learned a lot; they had even put in the plumbing.

"Do you think you and Jimbo would get too lonesome way off out there?" Because Jim was now hesitating.

"Oh, no-o," Jim breathed. "And my old jalopy is good for another ten years, sure. What's more, with that Hoot-Owl Hollow cut off, it would be nearer the boy's school than the house. But . . ."

"Don't go thinking up any 'buts,' " Harry said. "If you've got to be out in two weeks, you can stay in the cabin until you finish building. For my own reasons, I'm not going to be using it. You're welcome to it."

"But look here, sir."

"If it's a well and a septic tank you're worried about . . ."

Jim shook his head. Obviously they were not what were bothering him.

"Folks may not like it," he said at last.

Harry looked at him. "What business is it of theirs? It's my land and it's not in the city limits, so that zoning restrictions don't apply. Nobody's living anywhere around there— how can there even be any question of white section or colored section? I don't follow you. Why should anybody care?"

It was Jim's turn to look at Harry. "After the Supreme Court decision last May? People around here are very edgy. And they don't like me much anyhow, they never have. I wouldn't want to get you in trouble."

Harry had to laugh. "I'm already in trouble up to my eyes, Jim. A little more wouldn't bother me at all, but forget it,

there won't be any. I tell you, we're not stepping on anybody's toes."

There was a pause. Jim said, "I don't know . . . Maybe
you don't realize . . . I ought to warn you that I am a
member of the National Association for the Advancement of
Colored People, and . . ."

"Save it, Jim. I don't care a hoot in hell what you're a
member of. And I don't see that this is anybody's business
but ours. I'll go see Colin McDowell this afternoon. He'll
arrange for the land to be surveyed and fix up a deed. Let's
consider it in the bag."

"And you . . . think . . . Mrs. Hibbard will approve?"

Harry stared out over the yard. "It's my land," he said
quietly.

It was decided then. Jim's excitement, his happiness, was
a tonic to them both.

10

While Harry was of course aware of all the offers he had
received, from time to time, for his land, he still did not
quite realize the significance of this as viewed from any
perspective other than his own. He was possessive and
jealous where his land was concerned. Of course he knew
it was valuable land in itself and yet more "valuable" since
it lay between Peegram and Royall. He knew most of the
offers had been made by Royall executives. But instead of
thinking of the palaces they would put up as enhancing the
value of the surrounding land yet more, he thought of the
speed boats and the water skiing and all the ninnies who

would clutter up the river and said no, not only without regrets but as if such offers could surely not be taken seriously. He hardly knew—or only most vaguely—that Peegram people had their own explanation of his behavior; that he was playing it smart, upon Carrie's advice; that when the time was right he would sell soon enough . . . and make a killing. Harry was deflected by Jim's concern over getting *him* into trouble.

(In a small town, everybody knows everything about everybody else. There does tend to be that one little bit of a blind spot: the self. Though, in Harry's case, it was not so much a lack of self-knowledge as a lack of mirror-knowledge. The town was the mirror he should have paused to take a far closer look at himself in. It is almost the only self a little town can allow, after all.)

Harry's idea of trouble was that there might be opposition from Carrie, which he would have his fair chance to overcome (she might have a say in the Ford agency and she might have money invested in "a rival firm" of the Nu-Way, but she did not, by God, own his land); at worst, a wave of bad feeling which she, as the politician, might very well aid and abet, but which would blow over if he held firm, and which would touch Jim, the lone wolf, but little. Greatly outbalancing such a view of trouble were his thoughts of a home for Jim, his friend, who had squatter's rights on the river if anybody ever had. Harry had the sportsman's dislike of injustice and foul play; it was deeply ingrained in him. That Jim was being evicted, with no place to go, struck him as an injustice that could not be tolerated and that brought whatever trouble might ensue promptly into line. It was just far more practical helping Jim with a new and better home that nobody could take away from him than breaking Mayor Franklin's bones. And if Harry did feel that the keys of the gates of the arena might also have come miraculously into his hand, by way of Jim, it was not something to apologize to Jim for, but to thank him for. It would please Jim very much if Harry had found this way to bring his troubles to a head; give-and-take had always been important between them. *And you . . . think . . . Mrs. Hibbard will approve?* As if Jim and he, in some obscure fashion, were both going to get recognition at last.

Harry felt like an athlete who has been benched all season but who is back in the game. And if time had seemed to hang ever more heavily upon him, it now seemed to move with lightning speed, as events closed in.

Colin McDowell had been acting as Harry's lawyer for years; they had been at the university together. But Colin hedged when Harry went to see him that same afternoon. First, he behaved as though Harry were suddenly *non compos mentis,* completely out of his mind, and not able to conduct his own affairs. Then he said Harry would forever ruin the value of his land: nobody would build out there ever. Harry reminded him that every man has his own values. Finally, Colin said they would have to look up the original deed; that he was sure they would find a clause— of a contractual nature, of course; between the party of the first part and the party of the second part—agreeing that there would be no resale to Negroes, and which of course could only be interpreted as also to mean "no giving." Harry told him to go ahead and look it up—that there was no such clause (and there wasn't). He asked Colin to drive

out with him, so he could show him, roughly, the boundaries
of the land he wanted surveyed. Colin said he was terribly
sorry but the rest of his afternoon was solid with appointments. Harry asked him what time tomorrow would be
convenient; Colin said he had a case coming up in court
and couldn't say for sure but he would call him, Harry knowing full well whom he was going to call first. He didn't
waste any time about it. When Harry got home, Carrie's
car was already gone. He chuckled. Picked up *War and
Peace* in the best mood he had been in since his return. . . .

Carrie came back and he knew an unholy glee—because
she was visibly upset, that calm of hers out of joint. She
dropped a plate she was carrying in from the kitchen and
broke it to bits. Harry fairly leaped to help clean up the
mess—he got the broom and swept vigorously. Of course
she did not broach the subject to him; but this was important, neither did he to her. He whistled about the house,
offered to dry the dishes, forgetting they automatically
dried themselves. Went outside and joined the kids in a
game. She was not going to stop him. Didn't she know? And
know that *then* he could present *his* terms? . . .

Sixteen hours later, and the whole town knew Harry Hibbard was planning to *give away* a slice of that land, which
he had so steadfastly refused to sell to the cream of the
whites, to a nigger. They knew to which nigger. It was
either a plot or the worst piece of insolence since the days
of Reconstruction. Everything that Harry had done in the
way of trying to set himself up in business was reviewed;
his rebuffs, and the central reason for them, more subtly
reviewed, this section of the review including veiled allusions to a certain nigger's kin to a certain Southern lady,

and various theories as to the depths a "bastard" (ha-ha) might be expected to stoop to get his revenge. Come to think of it, it was very strange that a certain "bastard" had been hobnobbing with a bastard all these years. White folks weren't good enough for his precious land, but this particular bastard nigger was! The Supreme Court threatened the town from without, saying they should mix niggers up with themselves in their schools. And what *would* happen if the town didn't stand solid! But consider. A native son wanting to set up a nigger like a prince and, as everybody knew, give a nigger an inch and he'll take a mile. This Jim. He wasn't just Southern Womanhood's embarrassment—he was a member of the NAACP, an agitator and a radical, and the next you knew, niggers would be pushing the whites right out of Erwin Heights. Next you knew, they wouldn't just be ruining your schools, but setting themselves up as your next-door neighbors to boot. If it was the last thing they ever did, they had to show Harry Hibbard where to head in.

Eighteen hours, and Colin McDowell is calling Harry Hibbard up (according to his promise) and politely suggesting that Harry Hibbard find another lawyer with more time on his hands. The next two lawyers approached have no time either. This hardly matters—there are other lawyers. One does not necessarily need a lawyer to get such business transacted.

But the past tense is more suitable: twenty-two hours, and the Peegram *Inquirer* (published two afternoons a week) appeared with a long editorial on civic responsibility and the proper protection of property so necessary to Progress. On the front page there was also a brief news item to

the effect that it was *reputed* that a certain Madison real
estate firm, the Erwin and Davis Realty Co., Inc., was interesting itself in the possibilities of buying up Old River
Road land for the purposes of starting a "development."
What a great thing for Peegram if this were so. In Peegram
there was a crying need for a nice new residential area. This
issue of the *Inquirer* was not labeled EXTRA.

Forty-six hours, and that which was *reputed* came true.
Harry Hibbard received a visitation from authorized rep-
resentatives of the Madison real estate firm, it coming as
no particular surprise to him that the Erwin of the Erwin
and Davis Realty Co., Inc., was a distant cousin of his wife.
Nor as such a surprise that they should offer him (1) an
outright and fabulous purchase price for his land or (2) a
partnership in the firm, with the price coming to him in
stock, and since the development project proposed necessarily involved the opening of a Peegram office, Harry Hibbard would be there installed and could there consider himself top man on the totem pole. It was understood that a
certain contemplated deed of gift was to be dropped. Fully
apprised of his efforts to establish himself in business, they
dangled their prize at him with bland certitude. The news
of this offer and its refusal spread like forest fire through
the town, in unbelievable devastation to that which had
been upright and proud (and which must now, of course,
be more so).

Sixty-eight hours, and at Rotary luncheon Harry Hibbard
was cut dead by the men who had been slapping him on the
back since he was knee-high to a grasshopper; who had
yelled their throats raw for him in ball park and stadium.
Only Jesse Tate greeted Harry Hibbard warmly, calling

him "son," but not hiding and not trying to hide the magnitude of his concern. What did Harry Hibbard think he was doing? Deliberately destroying himself? If Harry Hibbard were behind the business side of a post-office window, now, nobody would buy a three-cent stamp from him! Seth, that Man of the Year, was not there—on purpose—to avoid the unpleasantness of avoiding—as Harry Hibbard understood it.

Seventy-two hours, and Jim was calling Harry Hibbard over the telephone. This was the conversation in its entirety:

"It's not going to work, sir," Jim said, his voice controlled and quiet.

Listening for overtones, Harry Hibbard said, "Are you all right?"

"Yes," Jim said. "But—"

"Nobody's threatening you or anything like that?"

"Threats or no threats," Jim's voice came back, "I'm prepared. I'm what they call 'dedicated to a cause'—I tried to tell you so. This kind of thing has to happen to open the door to a decent future for the people of my race. But in all our thirty-some years together, I don't think you've ever mentioned the Negro Problem to me once." His voice had caught and broke. "It's you I'm thinking of. I can't let you get any further into this."

"It's both of us I'm thinking of," Harry Hibbard said slowly. "I can't explain, but it means a hell of a lot to me too, Jim. If you can stick it out, I can."

There was a long, thready pause. Then: "I'm with you, sir."

"Right. I'll see you soon with the deed."

11

He got the deed the next day. He had already been busy about getting the land surveyed, had had to import surveyors all the way from Lower Creek. The lawyer who drew up the deed for him was a Yankee with somewhat the reputation of a shyster, true, but it was all done, all legal, and Harry had the deed in his coat pocket. There was the one problem (the one beauty) about it: it required Carrie's signature. He would now get that signature, he thought, as he was driving home from the lawyer's office. It was the climax they had been building toward.

When he turned into Rabbit Road, he saw that Seth's car was parked in front of the house. He had not seen Seth once since his return. Maybe the sum of Seth's contribution was sermons, he thought bitterly. *Come home and save us from her.* Carrie's car was in the garage. And were they then closeted together, chewing over his defection, deciding his fate, as they would suppose? Ah, after all, he would like to hit Seth.

He closed the screen door behind him, realizing that the murmur of their voices had broken off at the sound. He went on out to the side porch, took off his coat, hung it over the back of a chair, and had no more than turned around when he saw that Seth was standing in the door.

"Hello, Harry," Seth said.

Harry sat down. So *he* came as *her* ambassador, was that it? Looking cool, as always. Freshly shaved, showered and manicured. (Seth put him on the defensive; always had.)

Making himself comfortable (and decorative) in one of the wicker chairs; looking off meditatively (and appropriately) into the distance.

"You have sure been keeping yourself goddam scarce," Harry said. Seth habitually provoked him into an extra amount of swearing. Once Seth had contended that swearing was an expression of the religious impulse. Harry didn't know about that, but it did seem to be his way of communicating with Seth, this Man of God, this smooth article, who had never found God for himself. Didn't Harry know? Though the paradox sat so lightly on him now, without one trace, without one small scar of the sort that suffering leaves behind. But Harry's memory was long; they had not roomed together in the old days for nothing. If Seth did not, Harry still kept the picture in his mind of those nights—bitter winter nights they always were, in memory— when Seth, supposing Harry asleep, would get up out of his bed and go down on his knees before the open window where the icy air achieved permission to explore and devastate his mortal parts, causing his teeth to rattle and chatter—Seth, kneeling his way through night after night —with, sometimes, the chattered, anguished prayer reaching as far as Harry's ears: "Oh, God, help Thou mine unbelief—give me faith." Harry stirred restlessly as he looked over at the result who was so composed; who would be without calluses on his knees and who was glancing idly at *War and Peace,* which lay open on the glass-topped, wrought-iron table.

"It's *War and Peace,*" Harry said. "If you've read it, I'd like to . . . have you?"

Seth's eyes glazed over; he didn't say he had or hadn't.

"You know," Harry said, feeling his way into new territory (but, damn it, he still loved Seth, and he couldn't help admiring his frigging mind), "you know, there're some passages in the Bible I'd like to talk with you about some time. I don't get them at all."

"Yes?" Seth asked politely.

It reminded Harry of his own former relation to Royall Furniture. It was what you peddled, so of course the world had to turn around it. He supposed it was what happened to you when you took up something professionally, whether furniture or religion. You got off base somehow. You had to give the sales talk, the blurb out of the brochure. You laid on the adjectives. You not only couldn't afford to be sincere, but after a while you didn't even know what sincerity was in your particular sphere. There was no use to try to find out from Seth what rendering to Caesar what was Caesar's and to God what was God's might mean; or why Jesus had struck a fig tree dead for being without figs when it wasn't the season for figs; or anything else. It was quite likely he and Seth had nothing at all to say to each other any more. Why in hell didn't he go? Harry was not going to discuss his troubles with him, no matter how long he sat there looking appropriate. That was his forte, Harry supposed, listening to people's troubles. Passive about it. My God, it was hard to believe this was the same man who had preached that sermon which had gutted him!

No sooner thought than Seth was leaning toward him, the look in his eyes coming out to meet Harry, so that Harry's hurt was immediately eased. "You can't win, Harry," was what he said.

Harry met him halfway. He could not help himself, he

could not have done otherwise. He said, "I think I will."

"No," Seth said, flexing his hands in a curious fashion that Harry had not before observed and that must be new with him. "You're not playing by the rules. You can only win as long as you do play by the rules—surely, you ought to know that—as long as you abide by and obey them. You can't blow the rules, Harry, and expect to win."

He smiled his rare, boyish smile which had got its way with Harry so many a time. "I've come *to talk* you out of this," he said. "The word against the deed, Harry." (The smile again.)

"You mean you've come from Carrie," Harry said evenly. "You mean you'll say what she has told you to say."

They looked at each other.

"Let's you and I neither underestimate nor overestimate each other, Seth."

Their look held.

"All right," Seth said.

"All right," Harry said. "Go ahead. Talk. Talk me out of it. I'm listening."

"Did you have to pick *the race issue* to fight your most intimate and personal battles around?"

Harry said nothing. He tended to forget that nobody had ever supposed his and Carrie's marriage a happy one. That all his efforts to get out of the Royall harness and set himself up could be most blatantly interpreted. That instead of taming her—as some, anyhow, had hoped he would—he had turned on her in the sort of low and impotent revenge that made everybody have to take her part, sinking them in deeper than ever. He flaunted his impudence—trying to give away land that the bluest of the blue blood had offered to buy to her bastard Negro relation. And even when that was known, she had still most generously provided him the means of reconciliation which he had refused. But worst of all, he who had always overobeyed *them,* who had been as much their property as the railroad station restroom, threw defiance in *their* face! Threatened the established moral and social structure of the whole town! If he had not gone insane, what was the explanation? It was very late for an attack of male vanity and the desire to rule his own roost. Hadn't he been at her beck and call, at the beck and call of all of them for years?

"If only it were just a matter of bad taste," Seth said. "Merely washing your own dirty linen in public. . . . Harry, are you out to tear Peegram to pieces—and destroy yourself and your home and your wife and your kids—all—in the bargain? Is that what you're after?"

"No," Harry said. He did not elaborate.

"Well, that's what you're doing. That's what you've done unless you agree to drop everything as of this minute."

Seth paused—he waited. Harry lighted a cigarette.

"No," Seth said, "I'm wrong. It isn't 'unless.' I'll phrase it over again, shall I? That's what you would be doing *except* . . . Do you understand?"

"No."

"*Except* as you are not going to be allowed to."

"Go ahead, Seth. I like it when you talk straight. Would you care for a Coke?"

"No, thanks. Carrie gave me one."

"Then excuse me a minute. I'll get a beer."

He went to the kitchen for one and came back with it and sat down. "Now. Do go on."

Seth gave him a smile that was hardly the boyish one. "The Royall job of salesman is waiting for you. You'll sell your land outright; the price offered stands, though not the partnership. You've lost your chance at that. Nothing little or mean about withdrawing it. It's just that it's become necessary that you leave town for quite a long time, don't you see, until all this simmers down. Your reassimilation will have to be gradual, of course, and never again more than peripheral. Am I making myself clear?"

"I have a deed of gift for a piece of land in the pocket of that coat there that's hanging over the chair," Harry said. "It needs Carrie's signature. As soon as you go, I'll ask her for it."

"The alternative is divorce," Seth said.

Harry stared.

"You have been untrue—not just to a woman, but to a whole tradition, a whole manner of life. You've committed adultery in the worst way."

Had he? And why couldn't he indeed have settled for whisky and women, instead of the Gideon Bible, in all those hotels?

"Even in Peegram, when there's sufficient provocation, divorce is an acceptable solution, Harry."

Yes, yes, yes, Harry thought. Take Ray and clear out! Take him and clear out for good! Go where jobs grew on trees and . . . but he was forgetting Jim. Seth was watching him out of his cat's eyes.

Seth said, "But you'll probably want to understand in advance that there wouldn't be any question about the custody of the boys." He spaced his next words out a little. "She would get them—both of them—which is her intention, asking for them both—should you force her into instituting proceed-ings. There isn't a court in the country that would give their custody to you." He drove the last wedge of insult. "She will not ask for alimony or anything toward their maintenance. All understood?"

Harry could not have found his voice if he had wanted to answer. But one lone thought broke clear: she would not divorce him any more than he would her! Not when it came to a draw. Not in the final analysis.

Seth was not through. "If you've been getting any voluptuous feelings of gratification out of the notion that you're advancing the Cause of the Negro, rather than destroying one individual Negro, maybe I can help to set you straight. Have you—uh—heard about Jim yet?"

"I don't know what you mean," Harry muttered.

"About his losing his job. That's what I mean."

"As of?" Harry's voice clipped out now.

"As of this morning, I believe."

Seth flexed his hands, but Harry's hands were fists. When he had taken it in—that Jim didn't have his job—he said, "And you've had something to do with that, too."

Seth's shrug was very nearly imperceptible. "You didn't really expect he would be able to keep his job, did you?"

"I know this. I know I'll help him get another one."

Seth laughed. "*You?* In *this* town? *You* help *him* get a job? Ah, Harry, excuse me, but that is funny. I understand that the losing of his job may not be all that is in store for Jim. I understand—"

Harry cut him off. "Coming from you, Seth, a Man of God, that—you could only call it a threat—does not seem funny to me at all."

At which moment, when the tension between them was stretched as taut as steel wire, Harry saw Ray coming across the yard. He came hunkered over, stumbling. His hands were hiding his face and blood was oozing from between his fingers. Harry slammed out the screen door and was down the steps.

"Ray, Ray!"

He pulled down the quivering butterfly hands with the blood all over them . . . thank God! . . . it was only a nose-bleed and already stopping. He picked Ray up in his arms—Seth held the door for him—and carried him on through the house and up the stairs. "It's O.K.," he kept saying over and over.

He laid him on the bed. It wasn't necessary to pinch the soft part of the nostrils or pack them with cotton or anything —it had stopped. He went for a cold washcloth and wiped the blood away. There was a pretty bad bruise under the left eye, although far enough down so he wouldn't have a shiner. What could have happened? He took the washcloth back to the bathroom, rinsed it out and brought it back.

"Just lie still awhile," he said. "You're all right."

But Ray was keeping his eyes closed.

"What happened, boy?"

Ray's eyelids, cheeks, lips twitched. Harry waited. He reached down and ran his fingers through the hair that was too soft to be standing on end the way it was, as if in defiance of its own natural law. He brought only one word around those twitching lips. "Fight."

Strange, he should not have thought of this himself, for imagining some such disaster as occurred when he had used to take him fishing. But if there was a thing Ray was not made for, it was fights, and so far as Harry knew, he had never engaged in them.

"What was the fight about, son?"

"You."

Harry jerked his hand free of the hair he had been stroking. By God! He now watched all the twitching and twisting and choking as if hypnotized.

"They said you were a nigger-lover. They made up a song about it and sang it."

He does not ask me whether I'm a nigger-lover or not.

"So you fought them?"

"Yes."

"Was this the first fight? How long has this been going on?"

"Maybe about three days."

The twitching and the twisting became quieter. Harry gave him the folded washcloth and told him to put it over the lower part of his face.

"I'll be back," he said.

Going down the steps, he remembered one of those songs kids sang when he was a kid:

> *Nigger, nigger*
> *Black as tar*
> *Put your head*
> *In a molasses jar.*

Slight variation on the same? *Nigger-lover, nigger-lover* . . . How would it go, he wondered.

Seth was still sitting on the porch, poised, calm, yet flexing his hands in that curiously stricken way.

"Another fight?" he asked.

"I didn't know there had been the first."

"Forgot, I guess, the oldest law there is. The sins of the fathers visited upon their sons, always. . . . Have you come to your senses, Harry?"

"You'd better go," Harry said. "Do you mind?"

Seth stood up. "Haven't you *done* enough?"

"Haven't you *said* enough?"

On an impulse, they shook hands. Harry could not for his life have said what made them do it, when he had had it on the tip of his tongue—"Now, go report in." Which Seth did. He stopped off to see Carrie a few minutes before taking his leave.

It was desperate, very desperate now, and he would have been a great fool to see it as otherwise. He wondered if there was such a thing in the way of a fight where everybody is the loser. He was out in the kitchen, getting out the ice to fix Ray a cold drink. He had to think of the right words to say to Ray, he had to call Jim, he had to . . . get a signature.

12

Several hours later. The right words to say to Ray never came to him—words were Seth's department. Ray came down to dinner but ate so little that Carrie administered a laxative and put him to bed. Harry sat with him until he slept. Salvation? He kept thinking of the bulge that a baseball had made in an apron pocket. If the eyelids did tremble and the butter-fly hands did clutch the sheet, in sleep, the father had still to ask himself whether the son was not a thousand times bet-

ter off without him. Salvation in the form of cruel taunts and
a bloody nose? Or the narrow limits a loveless mother imposed? But the point was . . . (that if the father and mother
could *only* get together). . . .

Every fifteen minutes or so he had been trying to reach
Jim by phone, but getting no answer, though he made the
churlish operator let it ring long, each time. His impulse was
to rush out in search of him; but perhaps better to wait till he
had the signed deed in his pocket? First things first?

Carrie was in the den; she was sewing. (That she could
keep on sewing, and cooking, and so on, while she ran the
town, was of course a part of her pride and "position." That
she could keep up all the wifely show and still put the men to
shame—beat the men at their own game.) The time had
come, he knew. The deed had been "witnessed" in the lawyer's office, the lawyer's secretary being conveniently enough
also a notary. In Peegram, witnessing was pure form, so that
this was hardly considered irregular practice. Carrie's signature was its own witness.

He went out to the porch and took the deed, folded lengthwise, out of his coat pocket. He got out his pen.

He went back through the dining room and down the hall
and into the den and sat down in the leather chair, always
reserved for him and reserved for him now. Carrie looked
over the tops of the glasses she wore for "close work" and
smiled at him. It was a smile that shook him.

He unfolded the deed.

"I have something here I'd like you to sign," he said.

Her voice (it was a beautiful voice, the "Erwin voice") was
as clear as a bell. "Is that so?"

"Yes."

She put down her sewing. It was a tremendous moment. His heart was hammering against his ribs.

"And do you have a pen?" she asked.

"Right here," he said.

He was going to get up and take it to her, but she had already risen and was coming to him. He handed it to her. She sat down at the desk, switched on the desk lamp, and as if without the necessity for looking (such was her experience) found directly the place where her signature was needed. She raised the pen.

He had to hurry, because she was already bringing the pen down, and he was determined to get it clear—friendship and justice, rather than revenge; and, if she were yielding, the fact that he came not as the fool cuckolded and cringing before her own bold sweep to wealth and power, but as her husband.

"It's the deed for the land I'm giving to Jim," he began. "But—"

She cut him off. "Of course," she said, the pen now in position. "But it does occur to me . . ." She brought the pen back up, lifted her head and was looking at him over the tops of her glasses. "I'll be happy to sign it, of course," she said. "I'm simply wondering whether there's the need."

"Carrie . . ."

"What I mean is, I have heard that Jim has left town."

As he stared at her, his heart plummeted to his bowels.

"I mean," she said, "of course, it may be merest hearsay. But somebody did call me right after dinner and happen to mention it. So maybe you'd better check, dear, before I sign. I mean, if Jim has moved away, or anything like that, there wouldn't be any point in it, would there?"

"*If* Jim has left town, Carrie . . ."

But he stood up and went woodenly to the telephone and gave the operator the number and got no answer.

He went on out and got in the car and drove around there. The house was dark. He drove on to Jim's nearest colored neighbor's house and parked. He went up the path; knocked. It was Cindy, the cafeteria cook, who lived here, as he knew. She had been the cafeteria cook when he was in school. He had to knock again and call her name before the door was finally opened a crack (he heard the key turning in the lock on the other side). He put his foot in the crack as unobtrusively as possible. The sour secret reek of the house assailed his nostrils.

"Where's Jim?" he asked without preamble.

"Don't know nothin' about Jim," was the reply that came through the crack. It was Cindy's voice. He felt the pressure against his foot and set his shoulder to the door, widening the crack slowly. Now he could see her face swimming out of the shadows.

"Tell me where Jim is," he said.

"Got no truck with Jim," she said. "Neither seen him nor heard tell of him. None of we-uns has."

"Come on, Cindy," he said. "I'm asking you."

Then he made out Cindy's husband skulking in her rear. A loosely slung, garrulous Negro Harry had often seen hanging around the square.

"Where's Jim, Ross?"

"You, Ross," Cindy cried. "You keep your blabber-mouth shut!"

"I'm in a hurry, Ross. Where's Jim?"

Cindy set up a rocking and a wailing.

"Big black car," Ross said. "Fine car. White folks—gen'le-men. No sticks nor guns nor nothin'. Come and took Jim and Jimbo away. Dat's all, Mr. Harry, dat's all."

"Where were they taking him? Who were they, Ross?"

"We sure-nuff got no knowin' of any of that, Mr. Harry, that's a fact. We don't know and we don't calculate on findin' out."

"You never saw a one of those 'gentlemen' before?"

"No sir, Mr. Harry, I swear that on the Book."

"Thanks."

He got his foot out of the door before Cindy slammed it. Back in the car, he sat thinking a moment. Then he drove on around to the Esso station where he was in the habit of hav-ing his car serviced. He knew that Ernest, the young colored man who worked there, was one of Jim's only intimates. Under his breath, and swiping the while at the windshield, Ernest confirmed Ross's story. A black car had come with white men in it, these white men not being the rough sort. No guns or sticks or anything. Couldn't say who they were; strangers, maybe. But they let Jim pack some bags.

"They were just getting him out of town," Ernest muttered. "For his own good, like. He got some letters, Mr. Harry, tell-ing him he better. From Mr. Andy Boyd and his friends, we figured, though we couldn't be sure—the letters weren't signed. He should have gone himself. They just 'helped' him. He'll be all right, long as he doesn't come back."

"You have no idea where they might be taking him?"

"No, sir."

"Well, thanks, Ernest."

"Mr. Harry?"

"Yes."

"I . . . wouldn't try to find out too much right now. They might . . . you know . . . take it out on him."

"You mean the chances are they won't hurt him if I leave things be?"

"That's right. They'll let him go and Jim'll get on, he's smart —long as he never comes back here."

"I see. Thanks, Ernest."

Harry paid for the gas he had bought and pulled out of the station. They were licked, that was all. Maybe Carrie *had* maneuvered it. Carrie and Seth. No doubt. So what? If they (their agents) let Jim go, he *would* be better off away from here, anywhere else at all. Jim had the NAACP, he had something to live for, he could start a new life somewhere with Jimbo. With Jimbo. Yes, Jim had complete and indisputable custody of Jimbo. Jimbo was his legacy. . . . And should he and Jim have gone ahead with the deed, and got the house built somehow, they had only to burn it down. And *could* Jim and Jimbo have lived alone and unprotected, way off out in the woods? He shuddered to think what might have befallen them. *Let Jim go.* It is finished.

He was the one trapped—and no fault of Jim's! Could not save his little son. Could not stay and could not go. Could not accept her terms and now withdrew his own. This is it, Harrykins. Had *anybody* ever called him Harrykins? This is it, Buster. (And Fred knowing nothing of any of it.)

When he arrived home, he didn't go back to the den. Perhaps she sat there with pen still poised. He went on up to his room.

13

It was as if no time had elapsed since the time of his coming in and this time of his lying spread-eagled on his bed, holding a corner of the pillow in his mouth, as he had used to when he was a kid and his mother was downstairs. There was a kind of review of fence posts, television antennae, advertising slogans.

(Fred was not around.)

Fence posts, television antennae. He could not sleep, spread-eagled or huddled. Outside, heat lightning turned the sky on and off.

Sedge grass stood erect in a field and the dog was quartering the field and he had the second gun he had owned, the breech loader, with him. The dog (whom he did not recognize) came to a point and he went up and sent the dog in. The birds rose thunderingly. Their wings were black against the sky and he raised his gun.

Ponds, creeks, holes, rivers.

One river, the Big Peegee, the first river he had ever fished, and the only river he knew every riffle and every eddy of. His river, all its pools and reaches; his river with a No. 2 spinner, with a black gnat tied to a No. 4 bronze hook; his river with cane pole and worms. The wind freshened over the water. He fished it every way he had ever fished it. (He had never trolled it.) But he kept clear of his present boat, the fine six-teen-footer he had himself designed, with bow ending in a sharp point and three and a half feet in the beam, so that she drew almost no water, and that he had had fitted with the

Johnson outboard motor, that he might go more quickly up river, the twenty miles he liked to, cutting the motor then, and drifting back: fishing all his favorite pools and lay-bys. Every sandbar, every rotten log was his. But he would have nothing to do with his boat, preferring the awkwardness and the leaks and the broken oars of Jim's johnboat of long ago. On and on, without a strike. Cast after cast—no matter. He was not casting at random. That protruding log, with its deep shadows, concerned him.

Now he was on the bank, he lay on his left side behind the bushes and made dry casts until he had enough line out. The Big Mouth struck like lightning—the fight was on—he set the hook—the line went racing out. He warned himself: a Big Mouth will make a run with the line where your Little Mouth bores down. The warning was no good, the Big Mouth broke the line and was gone. The Big Mouth swam the ceiling, its gills breathing in the terrible oxygen.

No morning sun came slatting through Venetian blinds.

Bringing Carrie creelful after creelful. Sitting on the steps, cleaning them with his knife—his Barlow knife—he recognized that. But he was worried because he did not know what kind of fish they were. Intimacy between killer and killed. He cleaned Ray tenderly and took him in and laid him on Carrie's drain board.

Ah, she cooked so well, she liked to cook. And he liked to kill.

I am all the birds that I have killed.

Making meals out of each other.

He did not wish to contain death any more, he was not worthy of the trust.

He got up and went to the window and watched the lightning turning the sky on and off.

He went back to the bed and sat down on its edge. Immediately, birds began to wing their way through his mind—not quail, not grouse, not doves—flickers, orioles, cardinals and goldfinch, chickadees and wrens—birds he never never would have shot at.

He turned on the light on the night table. The Madison *Observer*, the evening paper, the one that was kept sacred to his touch, was lying there, though he did not know how it had got there. *War and Peace* was not there, it was downstairs, on the side porch. But the paper was. And the Bible was, the Gideon version that he had bought. He had no intentions of distracting his mind by trying to read the paper— he feared it had been put there with some dark purpose—but against his will his eyes picked out a little special feature contained in a box; the description of an Italian dish, said to be delicious: larks, served with heads intact and mouths open, as if singing.

He took up the Bible, which fell open (strangely) in his hands. And so, as if there were no help for it under heaven, he read.

> . . . In the day when the keepers of the house shall tremble, and the strong men shall bow themselves, and the grinders cease because they are few, and those that look out of the windows be darkened. And the doors shall be shut in the streets, when the sound of the grinding is low, and he shall rise up at the voice of the bird, and all the daughters of musick shall be brought low:

Also when they shall be afraid of that which is high, and fears shall be in the way, and the almond tree shall flourish, and the grasshopper shall be a burden, and desire shall fail: because man goeth to his long home, and the mourners go about the streets: Or ever the silver cord be loosed, or the golden bowl be broken, or the pitcher be broken at the fountain, or the wheel broken at the cistern. Then shall the dust return to the earth as it was; and the spirit shall return unto God who gave it. . . .

He went downstairs, found his way through the dark to the den where he did not expect to find her with pen poised. But it was good that when he had turned on the light, he did still find the pen. Pushing away that which took up room on the desk top, he sat down. Paper he found, as he had known he would, in the middle drawer. He began to write. Pain and labor were involved and his eyes kept straying toward the deed. *Dear Jim,* he wrote. But this came out, *Raed Mij.*

One time, in high school, he had distinguished himself by forgetting which team he was on and running with the ball thirty-five yards, the wrong way, for a touchdown. It wasn't Coach Perkins or his father who had been so furious with him; it was his mother. He remembered that for a week afterward clean socks were as hard to come by as the moon, that the cream for his cereal was sour and that his bed stayed unmade. It wasn't till three games later that she could face the neighbors again and so fully forgive him. He remembered he couldn't understand it at the time, when she didn't know the difference between a touchdown and a touchback and never did get straight what a first down was.

He could not understand how the crushing ordeal over an inflated dead pig's skin concerned her.

He studied his letter, which was only a page long and smeared in spots. He did not know how to sign it. He hesitated, then wrote *Sir,* which came out *Ris.* He folded it and put it in an envelope and sealed it and licked on a stamp that he found in the small brass box. On the envelope he should have written *Mr. James Erwin,* at least, and even though there was no address. But after a great deal of hesitating, he wrote simply *Jim,* which came out *Mij.* He took the letter with him, back upstairs, and when he had dressed, he put it in his hip pocket.

The heat lightning had stopped playing with the sky; it was getting light.

14

In the back yard, he was walking back and forth between the sycamore and the holly bush. The sky was no mackerel sky but blue and cloudless. Maggie, his bird-dog bitch, was sitting perfectly still in her pen, watching him out of her yellow eyes. He should not have kept her here had not Carrie taken such good care of her. Fred might work her, but Carrie tended her and fed her, and her law was such that the children left her alone, all but Ray. It was the one department of Carrie's law that Ray sometimes disobeyed.

"Maggie," he said. Maggie's tail thumped. "Eiggam," he said. Her tail thumped again. "Fool dog," he muttered, turning away.

Ray was coming around the corner of the house, applying

his bare toes to the grass, trying to pull the grass up, in separate blades, with his toes. He came as far as the steps and sat down. The bruise under his eye looked grotesque.

"Here," Harry said. He had found a fifty-cent piece in his pocket and he held it out.

Ray put out his hand. "Thanks, Dad. What's it for?"

"Oh . . ." Harry shrugged. He resumed his walk.

Out of the west there came one short crash of thunder. Harry stopped in his tracks. He looked up and saw that Ray also looked up. In a matter of seconds the sky gained weight, turned black from within and dropped a thousand feet. The trees became so still and so breathless that their former stillness was like commotion, by comparison. The thunder rolled. Maggie began to pace her pen.

"It's not thunder Maggie's scared of," Ray said. "Thunder makes her think of guns. It's the lightning that makes her howl. She won't howl till the lightning starts. She's only walking like that because she remembers that the thunder brings the lightning."

The thunder rolled.

"Sometimes," Ray said, "I go out and sit with her through a bad one."

"And get wet?" Harry asked.

"No, Dad. We get in the doghouse together. There's room."

"And does she howl then?"

"Not so much. She howls a little bit. For fun."

"To show off, you mean?"

"Sure. That's what I mean."

"Let's go in," Harry said.

They mounted the steps together and Harry hooked the

porch screen behind them. He closed the back door behind them. There was a tremendous crash of thunder, a long jagged slash of lightning, and the wind came in a great burst. . . . Carrie was ready for this. All the windows were already closed, of course.

Ray walked ahead of Harry down the hall and turned at the foot of the stairs.

"Going up?" Harry asked.

Ray nodded. The wind came screaming around the house and Harry had the picture of the trees bent double. Ray went up the steps, step by step, and disappeared. Harry stood there. The wind raged, but though it bowed the trees to the ground and broke their limbs and tore them out by the roots, it would not faze the house. It could whip the house, it could wrap itself around the house in all its fury and the house would stand. The house was sealed.

Through the living room door, he saw Carrie. The lightning showed him her face. But he had never seen that face, he had not seen it in the smile of last night. It was not hers. It was stricken. He advanced as far as the door and stood in it, waiting for the next flash of lightning that would reveal the face in all its meaning to him. She was sitting, holding her hands between her knees, with her skirt spread, as though she might have been, in secret, rocking herself. Behind her, the window; the rain coming in torrents, striking and smearing the panes, combining with the wind and the thunder to bring about his sense of growing deaf and mute. The lightning came. The face, or rather the expression on the face, was his own, that was all.

She became conscious of him standing there and they regarded each other in their sealed sanctum. She stood up, came halfway across the room toward him. He could not, but he thought he could hear her breathing.

She said, "I think I'll bake a cake."

He said, "I'll go fishing."

He was blocking the door; she would have to pass him on her way to the electric stove she would bake her cake in during an electric storm. Still, hers might prove the gesture. His would not be a mere gesture—he could see to that handily. He made her squeeze past him. In that instant, desire flared. He fumbled for the car keys which were in his pocket. Then he made his own journey to the front door and was gone.

Ray Hibbard

1

HE HEARD THE FRONT DOOR CLOSE ABOVE THE WIND AND THE
rain and closed the volume of his Encyclopaedia Britannica
in which he had been reading about zebras. He paused in
front of the mirror that hung above his dresser and explored
the bruise under his eye with the tips of his fingers. It was a
bruise that was shaped like a fig and it afforded him a certain
pride and a certain pleasure, in that if he pressed hard
enough with his fingers, it still had some of the hurt left in it.
But he would probably have to fight them all over again,
which was not good until afterward, when he could turn it
around in his mind so that he had won. Even then, he was
apt to feel the blood sticky on him. He did not understand
why they should be calling his father names suddenly, any-
more than he understood the upswelling of whatever-it-was

that was suddenly all around. He did not know what it was they thought his father had done, and while he might grant that his father was not being himself—reading that big book, reading to him; sitting around the house as he certainly never had done—he did not see that any of this was evidence of a crime such as the comic books and TV programs described. If his father had committed a crime, his father would have told him. He would not allow the name-calling or the nigger-loving song. When Fred came back, Fred would help him. He would just like to see them start anything with Fred around. He shivered slightly. It was a strange thing.

He went downstairs and searched the house but found only his mother in the kitchen. Climbing up on the high white stool, he sat and watched her making a cake. He could hardly hear the whirring of the Mixmaster, the thunder began to crash so. The lightning forked and zigzagged across the square of sky, framed in the window, which he could see from where he sat. He wished he had slipped down and gone straight out to Maggie's pen—for he could catch scraps of her howling above the uproar. He wished he had done that rather than coming here. Now he would have to ask her permission which she would, of course, not give. To pass the time, he counted between each burst of thunder and flash of lightning. For what seemed like a long time, he did not count higher than four. . . .

They would not let him go out to the river, so that he did not hear the shouts of the searchers, or the throb of the motors of the boats as they went up and down, dragging the river. He did not see the grappling hooks but only heard word of them in the mouths of the men who came to the

house and left again. The house filled with flowers and people
and food, ham and fried chicken and potato salad and pies
and cakes. It smelled loud of the flowers stuck so hard into
every vase. He had never seen so much to eat and he would
have liked to ask why it was a time for eating.

They did not let him go to the funeral. Therefore, Cousin
Elaine, William Morrison's mother, came and stayed at the
house during the funeral, while he and William Morrison
played marbles in the driveway, saying to each other, "Your
turn."

The picture of his father that he formed in his mind had
ribbons of green slime caught in the short, stiff hair and pools
standing in the body, the way pools stand in an uneven street
or gutter after a rain. The hands you could squeeze like a
sponge. There were no eyes, only holes, though he was not
positive whether this was because of the fishes or the grappling hooks. His mouth was open; his teeth stained greenish
with the slime, and broken off some; a small rock lay on his
tongue. This picture was at first very clear, then it blurred
and faded slowly, then it disappeared.

Fred did not tell his story when Ray was around, but Ray
had been eavesdropping all his life—on Fred and on Carrie—
and he did not stop now.

Fred and Fred's friends were playing cards in the cabin,
while waiting for the storm to wear out. Coach Perkins had
gone to town and was not there. Sometimes the card table's
fourth leg would buckle, Fred said. He said the fourth leg,
not the first or second or third. The fourth leg of the table
had just buckled and Fred and the boys were laughing and
leaning over to pick the cards up, when out of the window
Fred saw his father's car coming down the dirt road. The car

was coming fast, he said, and swaying in the ruts. He said
his father jumped out of the car and left the door hanging
open. He ran down to the landing to where he kept the boat
run up on cables under the galvanized iron shed. Fred said
they had been using the boat but had run her back up when
they saw the storm would break. Fred said he was still standing there, bent over, with the cards spilling out of his hands.
He said the rain was blowing against the window in such
gusts that he thought he might be seeing things. Well, he
was still standing bent over, he said, with the cards in his
hands, when he realized his father had already run the boat
down into the water, started the motor, turned her around
and was heading for the open river. He said he didn't know
why but he looked back at the car with the door hanging
wide. He and the boys went on playing cards, he said. They
played cards for forty-nine minutes, he said, before he would
admit something might have gone wrong. He said he told the
boys his father knew that river like the palm of his hand and
couldn't any little old storm get him down. Said that they all
saw he hadn't taken any rod or tackle. But he said he told
them whatever his father might be up to, whatever took him
out, he was sure his father knew what he was about. The
forty-nine minutes were according to his watch, he said. He
was crying.

Carrie began to talk to him, then, but in such a low voice
that Ray couldn't get the words, though perhaps he did get
something of the drift. Fred cried terribly. Carrie talked for
a long time.

2

As it happened, there were rods and a tackle box, belonging to the boys, already in the boat when Harry Hibbard took it out. The boys said so when they were questioned (they had all been talked to by that time), so although the boat was never recovered, this was satisfactory evidence to insurance adjusters that there had been an accident; that Harry Hibbard had gone out for the purpose of fishing and had been drowned while fishing. They found the sodden, undecipherable remains of something which might have been a letter in the hip pocket of the corpse, but nothing could be made out of these remains. When the casket was sealed, it was almost as if the casket itself were the envelope with the letter in it; as if then dispatched to the dead-letter department.

Fred had had to be immediately and brutally briefed: his father was not the hero he had thought him. His status had changed in the less than two weeks Fred and his friends had been keeping themselves at the cabin. They had got mutterings of this, to be sure, since the cabin was not all that isolated. Friends had come out and some of them had gone into town from time to time, but they had not understood the gravity of it and Fred himself had been spared their gleanings. It had to be made clear to Fred: that he could expect none of the benefits of the hero's son-in-mourning. He had held back the others in the forty-nine minutes of faith in his father, but that was due to ignorance. He must not go about compulsively repeating his story. The story, too, was better buried.

By general accord, Harry Hibbard was to be erased from the records (it was to be as if Harry Hibbard had never been); yet this erasure, at the adult level, was far from complete. There was a lot of compulsive talking by more than just the boys who had had a ringside seat, so to speak. After all, Harry Hibbard's name still headed the Honor Roll on the bronze plaque that hung at the high school; it was also on that other Honor Roll of war veterans, rather conspicuously so. And when he died, headlines appeared in all the big newspapers all over the state, because all over the state he was still remembered for his football feats. It could hardly be got around, it was a fact that Harry Hibbard was the greatest athlete Peegram had ever produced or was ever likely to produce. And a complete erasure, at the adult level, simply could not be managed. The compromise, of course, was to dwell on his great days as if nothing untoward at the end had ever happened. This Carrie encouraged (though she herself did not speak of him in any way after she had briefed Fred). She still liked to "talk poor," a mild form of torment she liked especially to inflict on those who were not as prosperous as they made out. She quite enjoyed, for a while, promoting the myth that she was left bereft and helpless. (Some men were unkind enough to observe that they better really be on guard now, or Carrie would use her new poor-widow role to fleece them entirely.) But even this compromise failed of complete success. When intimates of long standing got together, they were apt to find some reference to Harry Hibbard's last days cropping up. It was as bothersome as a small pimple on the backside. This everybody agreed in: Harry Hibbard's funeral was without a doubt the tensest and the most embarrassing anybody had ever attended. And had not Seth Erwin carried the whole thing off, it could not have been endured. Seth had really made the Bible sing that day, hadn't he?

It was the children of around Ray's age who did manage a complete erasure of Harry Hibbard. (This was true, but with the one exception of one child, trying, one time, to make it clear to one other child, why this had to be.) If the funeral was embarrassing, the adults were still too relieved over the timing of Harry Hibbard's death to adopt wholeheartedly their usual view of suicide and its stigma—that it commits the soul to everlasting hell and is therefore tragically evil and to be condemned. They did not exactly admit it but they felt that Harry Hibbard had done them a favor by so removing himself from their midst. And he did prove their point, that no good could come out of trying to overturn the established scheme of Negro-white relations. But the fact that Harry Hibbard had drowned himself weighed very heavily in the children's judgment, even if they didn't understand the fine points of death and, much less, suicide. Harry Hibbard had let Ray down and Ray was the one *they* had punished. That Harry Hibbard had withdrawn himself meant he was yellow. They had idolized him too, particularly William Morrison and Tad (who had still another nickname—T.P.) and the others with football and baseball hopes. It was not as important that around Harry Hibbard's name they had heard the race issue talked up and had had their first concentrated dose of hate and unreason on their parents' part. What was most important was that Harry Hibbard had handed Ray a bad deal. Who had ever heard of a hero getting in a tight squeeze and instead of fighting back, drowning himself? Ray, who was punier than any of them, had had to do his fighting for

him, and they did not like that. In retrospect, they found it
unforgivable. They hated Harry Hibbard now, without lies
and without palaver and without mercy. They stopped singing the song that T.P. had made up and by tacit understanding gradually took Ray over as their special charge. They
would not trade with Harry Hibbard in any way again. These
children were the ones who managed the complete erasure.

3

A few days after the funeral, Ray began to grow worried
about the future. True, he had always avoided grownups and
knew little of the affairs of the grown-up world, except for
what he had learned of them over TV. And while he had
always eavesdropped on Carrie and Fred, this was for the
most part done only when they were together, or when he
sensed they were trying to keep something from him, which
was very often, since they did not think he was old enough
for the simplest things, not even for the explanation of Maggie's howling when there was no lightning but a number of
interested dogs around instead. But Ray knew this much:
the man of the family was the one who worked and brought
the pay check home. From TV, he knew what a problem it
could be if anything happened to the man, even if he broke
his leg and had to lie in the hospital with the leg up in the
air on pulleys, and his wife sitting by him saying, "You
mustn't worry, dear." But the man was always very worried,
sweating sweat you could see out of the screen, and trying
to jerk his poor leg out of the pulleys. The wife might have
to go to work in a factory or do something even more noble

without complaining, while pretending all the time to the man that she was playing bridge with the neighbors. Usually, she had worked before she ever married the man and went back to her old boss and cried bitter tears (which you could see even better than the sweat) so that he hired her again, though even this seldom turned out well till the man got his leg out of the pulleys and came limping home as a surprise, since the boss was almost never noble. Ray knew Carrie never had worked at any time. He had heard her say so; she probably didn't know where to turn. And he did not believe they had lady-salesmen out at Royall. He remembered other comments he had heard Carrie make. Over the phone yesterday he had distinctly heard her say that if prices got any higher she would just declare if she knew where their next meal was coming from.

He could see Fred and him hungry, setting out for school with holes in their socks and those patches on their elbows. No lunch money. He could see the house being sold out from under them, the moving vans coming for the furniture. And Carrie, with no lemons for lemonade, and no cookies, so that the kids made up a song about it.

He tried to be more careful about his clothes; to say *no, thank you* to second helpings. He began to take nickels, two at a time, out of the collection plate in church. But he understood that none of this was enough. Therefore, having made inquiries, but without telling either Carrie or Fred, he went down to Front Street one afternoon to see Mr. Avery who was the Peegram distributor of both the Madison *Observer* and the Madison *News,* the evening and morning daily papers that almost everybody in town took. T.P. had told him Mr. Avery's office was in the First National Bank building and he found it without too much trouble, though T.P. had not told him to use the side entrance rather than the front. First, Mr. Avery asked Ray how old he was; Ray told him he was going on eleven. In that case, Mr. Avery said, he could not think of a single reason why Ray shouldn't have a paper route. What did Ray think Mr. Avery was in business for, if it wasn't so young fellas like him could shake a leg. Mr. Avery took him to Mr. Lambeth's drugstore and sat him down at the marble counter and bought him a chocolate ice cream soda, which he sucked through two straws, while overhead the big fan turned round and round, and Mr. Avery went into the booth and telephoned for a while. Ray did not like Mr. Avery any better after the soda; he did not like grownups. But he was intensely happy about his paper route and more diffusely happy about the soda inside him, of which he was reminded all the way home by burps.

His happiness was considerably dimmed when he found out that Fred had also been busy, had also been down to Front Street—to Repelius', Gentlemen's Ready-to-Wear—and had also got a job—as a clerk. It would be full time till school started, after which they would see, something might work out for late afternoons and Saturdays. Fred was so proud of himself that for a while Ray's own news stuck in his throat; he could not bring it out. Fred, who had just turned sixteen, was already proud enough, but now he was more proud. And he said Mr. Repelius had told him he looked older than he was! When Ray did let on that he had a paper route, Fred said he was *proud* of Ray. If he did know that two jobs would bring in more money than one, Ray still found all this difficult to forgive, nor did he even begin to try to forgive till bedtime.

Carrie was very pleased with her boys. She took to saying "my boys" over the telephone. Ray had his ear cocked for the plural. She said, "My boys are taking care of me," in her deepest voice. He was doing something she could brag on, which was a good thing; about the best thing that had ever happened to him, he guessed.

T.P. went with him on his route at first, but he learned fast and was very soon on his own.

On Sundays, Carrie drove him around in the car because, she said, the Sunday edition was too heavy for him to carry. (He did not, like so many of the paper boys, own a bicycle, all of his experiments with bicycles having proved disastrous.) She got up at five-thirty o'clock in the mornings, when he did, to fix his breakfast. He did not much like her taking his nobleness onto herself. But he got so he waited for the kiss he was going to get right before he left. He liked this kissing, though William Morrison said it made him sick when his mother tried to kiss him.

One Saturday, when he had finished his collecting and had turned in his week's envelope, he was going into the post office to read the notices of criminals-at-large that were posted inside on the bulletin board. (There were large rewards offered for tracking them down.) As he was going up the steps, he happened to see Mr. Colin McDowell and Mr. David Mull talking together and he heard Mr. Colin McDowell say, something, something, Harry Hibbard. He froze.

"Fact," Mr. Colin McDowell said. "It's just one hell of a lot of insurance—educational policies for the boys too. Except for the land, everything he had was in insurance."

"Huh!" Mr. David Mull said. "And she's sold the land already, I hear. No telling what she's got all that land and insurance money invested in by now. She doesn't let money lie around and cool off any. Insurance! There was a quiet invester for you. Well, sport, what I say is this. Old Carrie's made a killing out of *somebody's* death, pardon the pun. Makes her about the richest mister or missus anywhere around here, wouldn't you think?"

"Lord, yes!" Mr. Colin McDowell said, taking a cigar out of his pocket and tearing off the cellophane wrapper which came floating down to rest on the steps. Ray picked it up and edged away. He folded the wrapper carefully and put it in his pocket. He kept on going until he reached the First National Bank building. There, he went around to the side entrance and up the steps. Mr. Avery wasn't around but Naomi was, sitting at the desk, holding the telephone with her chin, the way she was so stuck on; saying "Uh-huh" and "Uh-huh" and writing on a pad at the same time. He took the coupon books out of his pocket, laid them on the desk and waited.

"Hey, honey," she said, when she had put the phone down. "How's the boy?"

"I'm quittin'," he said.

His next stop was the barbershop, where he told Dan'l to cut his hair off short.

"Crew cut," he said.

Dan'l coughed and spit and turned red and carried on; Dan'l almost cried.

"What's the matter with you, Dan'l?"

"Not one thing, son," Dan'l said. "Crew cut it is."

Ray kept his hand in his pocket, crinkling the cellophane wrapper, while Dan'l cut and used the electric clippers.

"Yeah," Dan'l muttered, talking to himself the way he always did; Dan'l always acted like a nigger. "Don't care what none of 'em say, none of 'em. He came in here, off and on, thirty years. 'Crew cut, Dan'l, GI cut between two old Army boys. How's the kid?' Christmas, it's 'lectric train for the kid, rest of 'em tipping big. It's this and that, all the years; it's Johns Hopkins for the kid. Don't care what none of 'em say, kinder heart God never made." Ray crinkled his wrapper.

When Dan'l was through, it looked as if all Ray's hair had disappeared, sunk right down out of sight into his head. It looked as if he might have turned bald.

Crinkling the cellophane, he walked home. Carrie didn't say anything to him about his hair when she saw him. Fred did, when he came home—Fred cussed him. Said Ray looked like something out of one of those antique photograph albums and that all he needed was knickers. Wanted to know what Ray thought he was doing. Either he looked like a daisy or an orphan, Fred could not decide which.

When Carrie was out in the kitchen cooking, Ray told Fred Carrie was the richest mister or missus anywhere around. He told Fred there was a great deal of money that would not ever get cold. Fred said he knew all that. What did Ray take him for—a stupe?

"Well, if you knew she's rich, why are you working?" Ray asked.

"How do you think people *get* rich, squirt? Sittin' around on their hands? Senators and bank presidents and all the big shots you read about in the papers—they *work* when they're young instead of fooling around. It's . . . People *like* it when you work. They think you're the stuff."

"You *didn't* know," Ray said.

"I did too know," Fred said. "How would I not have known?"

"Anyhow," Ray said, "if you keep on working after school starts, how are you going to play football?"

"Football!" Fred said. "Who wants to play football? I'm not playing any football. I got better things to do."

Ray was shocked. He could remember when Fred was captain of Junior Varsity. And, last year, a sophomore, hadn't Fred still been about star man on Varsity? *Wasn't going to play football?* Ray couldn't really believe that.

"There are other things besides football," Fred said, frowning, jerking around and heading for the kitchen. But he turned back. "What's all this got to do with you having your hair chopped off? That's what I'd like to know!"

Ray found he missed his paper route. He missed the feeling the streets had early in the morning, he missed throwing the rolled-up papers at the houses that stared so solemn at him but could not move to avoid his aim. He missed the slapsound, slap-sound the papers made, landing. (He did not miss the collecting.)

"Aren't you going to take care of your mother any more?" Carrie asked him.

"No."

She didn't say anything else ever.

Fred didn't give up his job when school started. He worked at Repelius' every afternoon, except Wednesdays, after school was out and all day Saturdays. He turned into a dude. He started wearing purple suede shoes and bow ties and a hat on the back of his head. He drove the Oldsmobile everywhere, as if it had always belonged to him. He even took to singing in the choir—front row.

Dinner would be what Fred liked. This was partly because Ray had decided everything Fred liked, he didn't. And since Fred liked almost everything, it was confining.

Every night after dinner Fred would yawn and act big, sitting in the leather chair in the den. He would always do his homework there, with Carrie sitting close by, sewing or something. Ray did his homework (when he did any) upstairs.

One day Carrie told Ray he mustn't touch the evening paper any more until after Fred had finished with it.

4

He had lost his fifty-cent piece, the one he kept in his pocket and never spent. He retraced his steps the whole way back to school. He looked over every inch of the yard and the playground and went up and down the hall. The room door was closed—he opened it—searched the corners and the floor, getting down on his knees.

"What is it, Ray?"

He then saw that Miss L was sitting at her desk looking at him.

"I've lost my fifty cents."

She helped him go through his desk. They even shook the books and turned out the contents of his pencil box. They looked all through the locker room. It was nowhere.

"It was the only one?" Miss L asked him, laying a hand on his shoulder. "I mean, another fifty cents wouldn't do?"

For a while he didn't answer, for thinking, for not wanting her to move her hand.

"It was the only one," he said.

Miss L took a Kleenex from her pocket and gave it to him.
"Wipe your face," she said.

Wiping it, he felt that it was wet.

"I'm going home now," she said. "Let's walk part way
together."

5

Sometimes he would see Fred, getting out of the Oldsmobile
(an Oldsmobile 88, it was), with one foot on the ground
and the other still caught under the wheel, pushing back his
hat with his hand . . .

He would put on his football things, which he had made
Carrie buy for him, including shoes, which he was not to
wear in the house. He would put on his things, togs, he
learned to call them, all but the shoes, and pose in front of
his mirror in a crouch, with his hands held out for the ball.

He did not play with Polly Taylor any more; did not go on
rock-hunting expeditions or conduct experiments with bal-
loons. He played football now, or touch football, every afternoon after school.

It happened that they redecorated the den and got rid of
the leather chair. Then, Christmas, they traded in the Oldsmobile 88 for a yellow Ford convertible for Fred.

One day Maggie was not in her pen, when he came around
the house, after school, according to his custom, to tell her
hello before going about his business. He could tell by the
signs that she hadn't gotten out; she had been taken out. He
was hanging onto the fence when Carrie came up. She asked

him whether he didn't want some cookies and milk. He did not. She told him they had sold Maggie, so she would be active and happy—who was going to hunt her around here?

That same night, he did not understand why he should, but while Fred was doing his homework with Carrie at his side, he made a tour of the house. This tour included closets and the bedroom that was now a guest room. He found that there were no guns or fishing rods or tackle boxes, not even in dark corners. When he slid back the panel of the closet in the guest room, there was no line of suits on the other side that were wiggly in the knees and elbows; there were no suits there at all.

He never saw the Oldsmobile 88 again. The dealer must have resold it in Madison or somewhere even farther off. Maggie, they said, had been shipped to South Carolina.

Either he played football at school or touch football in the vacant lot. It became a familiar neighborhood sound, his voice rising on the air with "Hike it!" He was always getting hurt. "You're a screw," William Morrison would tell him. Or he would say, "Just take it easy, you screw, don't try so hard."

Getting bigger was his concern. He began to try to eat what he didn't like, everything (except milk) which was supposed to make him grow. Once a week, he measured himself against the wall in the bathroom. He would tell William Morrison he had grown an inch that week. "Screw," William Morrison would reply. He wished at least William Morrison would learn a new word.

One day Cousin Elaine saw him and said to Carrie, "Why, Carrie, that child is a *shadow*!"

It made him furious. Even Miss L wrote Carrie a note. Shame on Miss L; he was surprised at her. He was eating all the muscle-building foods he could hold. He told Carrie so, but Carrie hauled him off to Doc Claywell's office and Doc gave him a tonic which he had never heard one word about over TV and which, as far as he knew, men like Ted Williams and Phil Rizzuto certainly *never* used. Doc also gave him a brown bottle of round red pills, which Carrie put by his place at the table and made him take.

One Sunday (Fred in the choir, front row, in a black *dress* with a white collar), he was thinking he ought to leave off stealing nickels out of the collection plate. Carrie gave him plenty of money, she had increased his allowance. But the nickels out of the collection plate felt more like his. He would keep on taking them, he decided, two at a time, though he was always very careful to put in the dime Carrie gave him especially for that purpose.

This Sunday, after the service was over, Cousin Seth was standing in the doors, the way he always did, shaking hands with the congregation, and he found himself wedged in behind T.P.'s mother. She was talking to Miss Annie Tate and he heard her say, "It is right creepy, Annie, young Fred Hibbard looking so much like you-know-who. Why, Annie, he's the spittin' image!"

Ray wanted to buck her in the knees. Outside, he found T.P. and picked a fight with him, ruining his Sunday clothes and bloodying his nose—really, he did not know how his nose could bleed so often and still be a nose. T.P.'s drawn-out name was Theodore Pauley, which William Morrison had once changed to Toilet Paper and later shortened to T.P. when they got reconciled. But to pick a fight with T.P., you had only to call him by this unabbreviated nickname, which, of course, was what Ray had done.

"It's a lie," Ray said, when they had finished their fight and he was bending over, holding his nose.

"What's a lie?" T.P. asked.

"I don't know," Ray said.

"What you need is a handkerchief," T.P. said.

"What I need is Toilet Paper," Ray said.

Which, of course, started their fight all over. And it had to be Fred who came up and stopped them! Ray did not look at Fred.

He held his shoulders higher and narrower (straighter and broader, he thought) every day. A scrimped look was settling over his face (tough, he thought). As for his hair, he went regularly and religiously to Dan'l, and his hair for all practical purposes had disappeared.

6

In the early spring, it was baseball instead of football. William Morrison was captain of the Reds. (There were the Reds and the Blues, made up of fifth- and sixth-graders.) Ray was on William Morrison's team. And while William Morrison never let him pitch or play any bases, unless they were *very* short of players, he always got to play, he played outfield.

He struck out a lot. He got so excited, waiting his turn, hefting the bats ("hefting the wood," he called it). Usually nobody laughed at him, nobody made any comment when he struck out. Usually, when he was hefting the wood, he was crying when he didn't know he was. And they knew he didn't know, they had found that out. So often they had to fight him for crying, had to hit him so he would have something to cry about, and when they fought him for crying he would always fight back, crying, to prove he was not. They would sometimes give him of their store of marbles or bubble gum. . . . When he did hit the ball, there was not usually any comment either, no over-raucous cheering.

One day he hit a two-bagger. Another day he snagged a hard grounder and threw it, with fair aim, to first. . . . He had got so he would move in fast on a hard grounder. When he was afraid he would miss it with his glove, he had got so he would try to fall flat on it, so that he had acquired many bruises of all shapes and colors. The Reds never accused him of being scared when he did miss the ball, which continued to be quite often. But it made William Morrison furious when he fell on a ball that way.

"Screw!" William Morrison would yell.

On his birthday, he had a party. He was eleven and measured himself before sunup. He made Carrie bake all his nickels into the birthday cake. (She washed them first.) He was terribly excited, though he had not counted upon William Morrison swallowing his nickel.

7

One night, Carrie found him standing in a corner of his room, long after he was supposed to be asleep.

"What are you doing?" she asked him. "Why aren't you in bed?"

"I'm learning how to sleep standing up," he said.

"Why should you want to do that?" she asked.

"Birds do it," he said. "Birds never do lie down. When they lie down, they're dead."

"But you're not a bird," she said. "Birds' feet are made a special way. Now, get in bed."

Instead of turning out the light and leaving, she sat down on a chair. Once she put out her hand and touched his forehead.

"Have you not been able to sleep?" she asked.

But by then he was almost asleep and did not consider that it was necessary to answer.

8

A certain Saturday afternoon, Ray and William Morrison were waiting in the vacant lot for the other kids to show up. There probably wouldn't be enough of them for real baseball; probably, they would play *catch-a-fly-you're-up* with the softball that T.P. would bring. They were squatting on their haunches, each chewing a grass stem. Ray's pants were short for squatting and his legs displayed a good many of the bruises he had got.

Suddenly William Morrison threw his blade of grass away.

"He didn't just take up with a nigger," he said. "He . . . don't you get it? He killed hisself, went out and drowned hisself in the river. That's what he did."

They stood up and fought each other. By the time the kids came and they had started to play, Ray had no idea what it was William Morrison had said or what it was that had made them have to fight.

9

He saw a sight, one early morning, when he was sitting on the back steps. He hoped the afterimage of the sight, in full color, would stay on in his head since so much seemed to be turning gray and watery.

He was sitting on the steps. The sky was intensely blue. Because it was so early, the birds had the world to themselves. But before long, Mrs. Brittain's black Persian cat came walking across the grass, picking up her paws and putting them down. Ray hissed at her but she paid him no mind and the birds began to call their urgent, complicated warnings back and forth. All of this was going on at once when down out of the blue sky came a blue jay in a dive, like a jet plane, screaming as it came, aiming straight for the cat's head. Ray held his breath—knowing the jay must pull up—but the jay did not! Not before it had gored the cat's head with its strong black bill. Mrs. Brittain's cat reared and clawed the air. True, she continued on her way, but very hurriedly, and her fur was standing up so high that Ray could see the sun through it. He tried to memorize this long blue screaming flash. He hoped to be able to put himself to sleep with it.

10

On every hand, he had been refused permission to remember. Everything had conspired against it. After the slow fading of the mental picture of the drowned body of his father that he had formed, there was no shape or image of his father inside him. He might have found his father again by looking at Fred, but he could not do that. As far as his mind was concerned, the climax around forgetting was reached. The body had to take over where the mind left off, assuming the burden of "remembering" and defending the father, through crew cut and football and baseball and such, and the body, not being very robust, was now showing signs and sending out warnings of acute exhaustion. The trouble was, the dream of the father did not have the image of the father at its center, and so held him in gray, watery confines. And in spite of all the children's repeated efforts to attract him to the shore— hitting him to make him put his feet on dry ground—it is probable that since his release had to be around full and conscious remembering, and since such remembering was also exactly what the children, as well as his mother and brother, had to forbid him . . . it is highly probable that nothing would have availed, if a kind of accident of topic and circumstance hadn't served to churn the gray waters from the bottom. Of course, it was this very churning and parting of the waters that he was so afraid of at night. But this was different, this was not nightmare, this was real, and it was not the body, with the holes for eyes, that surfaced.

It happened on a certain afternoon at school, which began like all the other afternoons at school, and was no different from them until after he had half heard, and from a great distance, William Morrison say, "About this here Supreme Court decision" when the room was, without warning, overturned in noise and confusion, and various voices came piercing through his solitude.

"My dad says . . ."

"My mama said . . ."

". . . Africa where they come from!"

"Blood is gonna flow, that's what."

He hardly followed, nor did he follow the slow, soft course of Miss L's words that went on and on. It was abstracted chunks of words that seemed to be beating against him through the watery grayness.

The South was where the Negroes. As if inside us there was a second battlefield. Negroes. Maybe it's our turn. Negro children with us.

To steady himself he wanted to put his head down on his desk, but instead, he seized his seat with both his hands.

It was most distinctly that he heard William Morrison say, "You mean, Miss L, you're *for* de-seggergation?—Intergation?" And while he did not hear her answer as distinctly, he pitched violently against the frozen silence that followed. He saw her turn away and start flipping the maps on the map stand, heard William Morrison's quasi-whisper, ". . . Folks'll get sore . . . Anybody goes out of here . . . They'll say she's a nigger-lover and *we* know Miss L's O.K." If he did not hear T.P. backing William Morrison up, that was for trying to deal with the impact of *nigger-lover* at this juncture. He saw Miss L turn back around and smile and he heard her say, "It's not a secret. What I think and believe isn't a secret."

He stood up. He said, "Dogs don't care. Dogs don't even know *which* is white and *which* is black and *which* is spotted. Dogs don't stick up their nose at another dog 'cause he's a different *color*. So if they don't care, I don't care. Black is good as white. Dogs got more sense than *most* folks."

He knew his hands were clenched and, for the first time, he understood he was crying. True, he thought it was Maggie he was defending, but outside, once his fight with William Morrison was concluded, and he was going home, a song came pushing its way up, up, up, until it burst in his brain.

> *Nigger, nigger*
> *We hold the trigger.*

> *Nigger-lover, nigger-lover*
> *Run for cover.*

> *Coon, coon*
> *You die too soon.*

> *Coon-lover, coon-lover*
> *Join your bro-ther.*

> *BING, BANG, BOOM.*

It was not remembering itself that was thus immediately accomplished, but a barrier to remembering was overcome. It was as if he could make out the suggestion of light hovering around the edges of the formerly impenetrable and unmeasurable grayness.

11

In the days that followed, he became famous. People stared at him, dropped their voices or raised them sharply when he came near; pointed him out to one another and looked after him when he had passed on. At school, some of the teachers viewed him with an alarm and a distaste that they made no effort to conceal. People—adults—thought it curious, almost rude, the way he acknowledged their stares. Some few of them stopped him on the streets and asked him to repeat what he had said about folks and dogs. He repeated exactly what he had said, and not looking off vaguely into some distance of his own, but looking at them closely; as if he thought that *he* might be the one judging *them;* or might at any moment ask *them* to repeat something for *his* benefit! A change had come over him.

Carrie did not take him to task for what he had said, she never let on that she knew anything at all about it, but he was the one who suddenly would not let her alone! He would follow her about the house, stand regarding her with that new strange look of his, when she was talking over the phone or was about some routine business, such as rinsing the dishes before putting them into the dishwasher. It was almost as if he were allowing her a chance to make herself clear. Indeed, a lesser woman might have become unnerved in the face of such extraordinary behavior on the part of a son. One day he said in a quiet voice, "And where are Jim and Jimbo?" As a matter of fact, she did drop a glass that shattered.

And when, the second or third day after he had spoken his piece and achieved his fame, Fred came on him, came bursting into his room, face stiff with rage and something besides rage, he did not cringe, and he did not look either around or over or under Fred—he looked at him directly.

"Why, you little . . ." Fred said. "Goddamn you for a little farting no-good son-of-a . . . Why, you open your mouth again and I'll . . ."

He didn't open his mouth; he opened the door and in the most poised fashion silently invited his brother out. . . . Oh, he was steadily building toward something, he didn't know what, but the fact that he didn't know what did not deter him.

William Morrison founded the Junior Citizens' Committee and Ray went to the meetings. William Morrison was angry with Cousin Seth, his father, who, as chairman of the school board, was responsible for the firing of Miss L as a nigger-lover. William Morrison said if his father was chairman of the board, he was going to be chairman of the committee that would show his father and the board a thing or two. And, William Morrison said, he now inclined somewhat towards Miss L's and Ray's views of the Negras, but that to admit as much was no way to approach those stinkers on the board, and that therefore Ray must promise to keep his mouth shut about the real thing. Ray agreed that with adults this was probably the correct procedure and he offered to spiel off some multiplication tables when his turn came. The kids approved and were dubious only in that they did not believe Ray knew any. Ray said he would learn some, that that would be simple. Then Miss L had to come and break the committee up!

Looking straight at Fred had not after all caused his father's image to materialize, but *everything* was pushing, pushing. People kept staring at him, he staring back. *How did he know about Jim and Jimbo?* About friendship and justice? Carrie's words to Fred which he had overheard but had not been able to catch . . . was it that "something of the drift" of these words was coming back, delayed? Framed by people's stares? And combining with an also-delayed re-

turn of William Morrison's *didn't just take up with a nigger,
killed hisself, drowned hisself in the river* and various scraps
of talk of those like Mr. David Mull's and Mr. Colin Mc-
Dowell's, and Dan'l's, as well as the stiffness of Fred's face
and the glass falling from Carrie's hand and crashing—all a
piecework, by little and little, fitting together and pushing
toward that one moment when an image would leap clear.
(The image *they* would have erased.)

Absoluteness and implacableness of judgment, so typical
of children around his age, and heavily underscoring their
definition of an act of drowning the self as being yellow . . .
maybe this judgment of the act as yellow had been his own
child's judgment, but with the difference that it was also
that which he had had to fight most bitterly against admitting. And now, maybe this judgment itself was shifting out
from under him, in that he had now come too close to experiencing the breaking-point of human suffering to sustain it.
Maybe he had acquired compassion beyond his years. Till
now, he had always seemed so young for his age, not just
physically, but mentally, his poor opinion of adults doubtless
affording him no particular desire to emulate. But was this
the baby who had wanted all his nickels baked into his birthday cake? It was hard to believe that he could have done so
much maturing in the space of a few days. Yet now he
seemed older than any eleven years. He had stopped counting his bruises; stopped most of the compulsive rituals he
had developed trying to fend off the watery grayness—counting bruises, vainly or successfully calling up his blue jay,
snatching at the fantasies around his prowess at baseball
that were supposed to spike the gray intervals between one

time of hefting the wood and the next. Everything was pushing!

The night before the big game with Lewisville he felt very nearly guilty because the game was not assuming the tremendous proportions that it should. He recognized that he was especially excited but not about the game, not even when he reminded himself that Red had promised William Morrison as captain of the Reds and Ray as his sidekick that, providing they behaved themselves, they might sit on the sidelines with the team, which of course was a great honor.

At dinner that evening, except to tell him to take his pills, Carrie did not speak to him and neither did Fred. He regarded them attentively as they talked together about Repelius'; about what lines old Reppie better stock if he really was planning to branch out. Ray kept looking at them in that strange new way of his and looking at the table, at the way it was set, salt-shaker and pepper-shaker, knives and forks, platter and vegetable dishes and Worcestershire sauce. Remembering quivered all through him, yet still just short of fulfillment. And as he listened to their talk, he felt it drawing tighter and closer—not tighter and closer around him but tighter and closer against him, shutting him out, this shutting out also seeming to be something just short of fulfillment which went on and on and must never be allowed to stand still or drag. Almost as if they knew all about the pushing up inside him and could only keep pushing it down.

He excused himself with dignity and went to his room. There, he closed the door. At first, he walked around the room, picking things up and putting them down. Then, for a long time, he stood looking at a globe that was on his desk. Slowly, he went over to it—pressed a button that was

in its base. A light inside it came on. He bent over it, probing it with that look of his. Slowly, with his fingers, he
stroked the various countries.

He turned on his toy chest and in one passionate movement, lifted the lid. He began to take out books, one by one
—*Arabian Nights, Robinson Crusoe, Gulliver's Travels, Treas-
ure Island, Alice in Wonderland.* He took out records, also
one by one. He neither opened the books nor put any of the
records on his record-player, but he set them all around the
room with care. He was ready now. Obeying to the letter
Carrie's law, he went to the bathroom, brushed his teeth,
took his bath, washed behind his ears and went to bed.

12

But, that night, it was only that he slept as he had not, in
weeks and months. The moment of fulfillment, the moment
the image would spring clear of the grayness bringing his
release did not come, though as he walked to school there
was no abatement of his excitement and confidence that it
would. It was as if the grayness were all atremble with the
hovering light and that the inevitable breakthrough would
dispel the watery grayness forever. Oddly, on his way to
school, it was "I Pledge Allegiance" that kept repeating itself
in his head. "I pledge allegiance to the flag of the United
States of America and the Republic for which it stands, one
nation under God indivisible, with liberty and justice for all."
To the rhythm of his walking. His head up and his eyes
proud.

But the moment of his revelation probably could not have

happened anywhere other than at school. Partly, this was
because his father's disgrace had been public, with the defaming of his name a public defaming and its consequent
erasure a public erasure, so that any setting straight had to
be public and private both. Partly, it was because—since his
home was not of the most loving sort—he had that peculiar
and drastic dependence on the children who had taken him
over and for all their efforts to save him, made him run the
gauntlet. If Harry Hibbard was heroic *to the end,* it was to
them, as well as to himself, that he had to prove it. Had to
prove that he was not a son without a father, nor a son trying
to live his father down, nor a son trying hopelessly to fill the
father's bill (not any more)—he had a permission to discover
himself arranged meticulously in his room, which none
other than his father had given him and, almost, he understood this consciously.

In terms which he could not have expressed but was on the
verge of grasping, what he had to do was to demand and
receive a proper and honorable burial for his father, one
which he had earned for his father, and one which he would
not only make all arrangements for but also conduct, so that
from now on his father and he could rest, his father honorably dead and himself honorably alive. . . . But that it was
not so much he who had the power to restore his father to
the other children as it was the other children who had the
power to restore or refuse to restore his father to him, he did
not understand at all. He mistook his own change, his own
experience with suffering and his own attainment of compassion, for their change. And since he would by no means
say to them, "My father did *not* drown himself," but instead,
"My father drowned himself and it was all right and so you

will accept it in the heroic context," they could only do what they did. They could not unerase what they had so absolutely erased. And they could hardly agree to paint over the truth (as they saw it) with such a lie! Maybe they did feel a little differently about Negroes now, some of them, but that was never paramount in their judgment of the hero who had welched. They would not have cared had the fight been over his right to keep chickens in his back yard, he should never never have given up once the fight was on. Never should he have cheated on Ray, never should he have left Ray to do his fighting for him, which wasn't Ray still doing in a way? So that, to the last, it was Ray they were saving. And what they did not consciously assign paramount importance to, they could not be expected to take into conscious accounting, which was that it was indeed around Harry Hibbard they had received their first dose of massive adult hate, so recently revived around their dear Miss L, and that what Ray asked of them was more than what William Morrison had asked in forming the committee. What Ray asked was treason against their own fathers and for what they stood and without William Morrison's wit or ideas about "correct procedure"; without his security or right to sly defiance of a father who was a big shot and which had pleased them so. A son can defy his big-shot father, but he cannot condone his coward-father—there is all the difference in the world. It was either them or him. . . .

The morning passed for him—with everything pushing, pushing—and with the contagion of their excitement over the game and his own excitement merging.

It was both a long time and no time before they were picking up papers, putting away their books, tidying their desks.

Then Miss L was sighing and saying there were still without question fifteen minutes left. She suggested they discuss what they would like to be when they grew up.

Lester said he would be a banker, so he would always have plenty of money. Louise Pierce said she would be a model, since she had red hair and green eyes. William Morrison sent a note to Lester, which Ray passed, and which said, *She is rong. She has got greene hare and red eys!!* T.P. said he would be a peanut farmer.

Ray was ready. He raised his hand. He was afraid Miss L was never going to see him and say, "Yes, Ray?" He stood up, as he had done to speak his piece on folks and dogs; this was a continuation. At first, although this was a surprise to him, no words came. There was some scraping of feet and some shifting about in seats. He swallowed two or three times.

"I'm going to be a football player," he said. "All-American." Why did he put it like that? Even as he knew—no, *almost* knew—he need never try to be one again. It was a part of the shedding of the oppressive weight of the obligation of all these past nine months—he had his bruises, like medals, to turn in. And in the shedding, in the shifting from body memories to full mental remembering which would bring with it release rather than enslavement, it was as if a formal subscription to that enslavement had to open the way. Also, he had to get the total image properly before them and him, the image they had erased and he had pursued in living death. Of course: it was the accomplishment of mourning!

"I'll be a baseball player too," he said.

"And a furniture salesman." (He hardly heard himself; it was like walking up steps to the highest landing.)

"I—I'll be for liberty and justice for all, black and white."
(He took in his breath.) *I'll be like my dad.*

His dad. Had anybody around here ever heard of his dad?
Whatever he would be, football player or Arctic explorer, he
would be like his dad in the real things—that was it! *His dad*
crossing his lips at last—bursting and exploding—and yet?
He did not sit down. He stood there, trembling. But if he had
his feet on high and solid ground, they returned him to the
watery grayness, they returned him to the dream that was
without reality at its center. They had seldom laughed at
him; they did not now. It is possible that they had a glimpse
of his helplessness, and theirs.

It was from a distance he heard the bell ring and heard
Miss L ask him if he would stay a few minutes and help her
erase the boards. It was from a yet greater distance that he
heard her say, "Ray, your father must have been . . ." He
wool-gathered, he gave the board his one feeble downward
swipe.

"Can I go now, Miss L?" he asked.

"Yes, dear," she said.

13

Outside, leaning against the wall, William Morrison was
waiting for him. They did not speak. On their way to the ball
park, according to their earlier plan, they stopped for hot
dogs and Cokes, but Ray did not do very well by his, and
William Morrison said he was not very hungry either. They
continued on their way in silence. Finally, kicking up the
gravel where they were walking, William Morrison said, "I

don't reckon any old man is so hot—I found that out. I hate mine. I wouldn't be like mine for a million bucks."

Ray said nothing. They did not fight. It was more that a great tiredness had come over Ray than anything else.

He was sitting down on the end of the bench with William Morrison. As it turned out, it was not the same bench the players were sitting on—not even the second string, as William Morrison observed. At first, they were both silent and inattentive. William Morrison said it occurred to him that it did not matter for spit who won. But as the game went on, William Morrison, as captain of the Reds, became increasingly involved. By the third inning, when Peegram commenced leading, William Morrison got carried away. In the fourth inning, he bought candied popcorn, forgetfully wiping his hands all over Ray's pants instead of his own. In the sixth inning, the sparrow was hit by the pitched ball and slapped down. Ray saw this and he saw Tom Carter, the shortstop, pick it up by one leg and fling it over the fence. Ray closed his eyes then but did not see his blue jay screaming down. This bird, so little and grayish-brown; it almost seemed to him that this bird was his jay and that his jay had lost all its power and all its color and would never come screaming down again. . . .

"Red's not in this ball game," William Morrison said, giving Ray a dig in the ribs. "He's lost all his screws. That was his *curve* ball he just threw."

At the end of the seventh inning, William Morrison bought a Nehi Grape; Ray did not want one. In the eighth inning, the score stood 7 to 3, Peegram leading. There were two outs, Lewisville was at bat and in no time, thanks to Red, for whom William Morrison was ready to buy a one-way ticket to Alaska, he said, the bases were loaded.

"Oh my gosh, oh my good grief," William Morrison moaned. "And that great big yahoo is up!"

Ray was almost knocked off the bench by William Morrison, yelling and beating on him. "Oh my gosh, oh my good grief, oh my mama's gravy!" (It seemed that the great big yahoo had struck out.)

Ninth inning. The score was 8 to 3 when Lewisville went up in the last half. If only that darned Red kept his britches on, the game was won, William Morrison said. There was much general excitement: a Lewisville yahoo had stolen second base.

"I can't stand it," William Morrison said.

When the foul ball came their way, William Morrison yelled, "Duck, you screw!" and made a grab for Ray as he ducked himself. In that instant that Ray saw the ball, instead of ducking, he stood up, with his hands coming up and out from his sides.

In the stands, people rose. Coach, players, umpire came rushing over. William Morrison was holding Ray in his arms and whispering, "You screw, you screw." Ray explained that he was not hurt, though his neck did feel jarred. In a minute or two, everything subsided, players returned to their places, the game went on. But William Morrison was staring at Ray.

"You *didn't* duck," he said.

Peegram had won, eight to five. Players tossed their caps in the air. Fans came swarming down out of the stands, Fred Hibbard among them. Fred came pushing his way through the crowd toward Ray, speaking to nobody, and when he reached Ray, he seized him by the shoulder.

"I saw you!" he said.

He pulled Ray along, swearing at him, and in the crowd, they lost William Morrison.

"Where's William Morrison?" Ray kept saying over and over.

"You haven't got the sense you were born with," Fred said, shoving him into the yellow Ford convertible and slamming the door. "You just wait till I get you home."

"Where's William Morrison?"

Fred gunned the motor and they went roaring off.

"Look at that bump on your head. It's the size of an egg already."

It registered as a shock, that Fred was crying.

"Don't cry," Ray said.

"Goddamn it. Who's crying?"

The tires whined around curve after curve. Ray leaned out the window and vomited. Fred was turning into the driveway.

"Don't you move," he said.

He got out and came around to Ray's side and opened the door and scooped Ray up in his arms and carried him upstairs, swearing and crying. Carrie had appeared from somewhere in the house and followed them up the steps.

They undressed him and put him in bed. He kept his eyes closed. They tried to feed him some soup but he vomited it. Doc Claywell came. There was talk about the hospital and X rays. He kept his eyes closed. They moved him from his bed to another bed and carried that one down the steps, as he could sense, and outside, putting him, as he lay on this new bed, in an ambulance which swayed and rocked him gently. He sensed that they were going through some doors, into the hospital, as he would suppose, but he kept his eyes closed.

There was a great black burst which caused him to open his mouth. He sank down lower and lower until, in his dream, his dad was there. His dad said, "Take it easy, son. Don't run." Then they had got the boat down, they had turned her around and, in his dream, they were heading for the open river.

PART THREE

Fear ye not, therefore,
ye are of more value than
many sparrows.

Martha Lyerly

1

HE HAD NOT TOLD HER ABOUT HARRY HIBBARD. HE HAD MADE A
convulsed movement toward the ignition keys and started
the car, backing wildly over the weed track and driving like
one possessed back to town. She might much better have
heeded Roger and not asked Seth Erwin that question. It
was most certainly what had brought their meeting to an
end. He had not spoken to her again until they reached the
school, when it was school business they had attended to.
Now it was Monday noon and she would never see him or
speak with him again.

Her sessions with the substitute teacher were concluded,
her records completed, the report cards tentatively made
out, Mrs. Josiah settled with, the children told good-by, the
task she had dreaded so, though it had not turned out to be
as difficult as she had feared—there is a fatalism in children,

she decided. Her bags were packed and standing side by side on the scatter rug. Her bus did not leave till five o'clock, that was all.

It would be Roger who would come for her and drive her to the miserable little station with its dirty walls and its two facing rows of desperately individual seats, so decrepit they leaned in every direction; with the No Loitering, No Soliciting sign, no news stand, but a bubble-gum machine and a "Your Wate and Fate" scale, on which she had weighed herself the day she had arrived in Peegram: she remembered it so well. Roger would not leave her in the station. He was not the sort who dropped you off and had somewhere pressing to get to. He would come bearing candy and magazines. Not only would he be there when the bus was called, he would still be there when the bus pulled out; still there, maybe still waving, after the bus was gone. And that it would not be Roger's face she was seeing, as she waved back, Roger was also the sort dimly to surmise.

She should have spaced out her packing. She found pencil and paper in her purse. For a few moments she sat doodling aimlessly. Then she wrote down the number 365 and multiplied it by 24. The result was 8,760, the number of hours in a year. This she multiplied by 25, her age, and the result was 219,000, the number of hours of her life. She turned the sheet of paper over, wrote down 219,000 and drew a circle around it. She calculated that by stretching it a little she could say she had been with Seth Erwin two hours out of this total. Say she lived to be 65, that made the grand total of all her hours 569,400.

She returned paper and pencil to her purse. It was not her intention to tour this room again. She lay down on the bed.

He had not once touched her, the closest he had come was putting the cigarette between her lips. *Oh, death of all my life.*

"May you be damned, Seth Erwin," she muttered. "May you and all your kind who live by denial know all the torments of hell."

. . . Visited by a brief vision of the wrong man she would be forced to settle for, with maybe eyes *like his,* or a frown *like his,* which she wouldn't herself realize, maybe, for ages.

Teaching, in and of itself, would never be enough after this. Ah, she was sorry about her father's investment.

As if indicating that only it could see her through, anger seized her. He would never come away with her, never divorce his pristine wife. He was *committed* to staying here, committed to the pale and exotic flowering of his own death. And the unforgivable sin was—he loved her. She had seen, she knew. He would get his satisfaction from laying that love, too, on the sacrificial altar and offering it up along with everything else. The ashes he could present to himself as the prize. Sacrifice and denial to the end. Happiness would colic him, wouldn't it? But some lines from one of Rilke's "Duino Elegies" rose in her mind, gravely insisting that they were the answer. Oddly, they came back to her, not in German but in English, in her own rough and approximate rendering. "For Beauty's nothing but the beginning of terror that we're still just able to bear, and the reason we adore it so is because it serenely disdains to destroy us. Each single angel is terrible. . . ."

She was crying again. Oh, no, I don't understand. *Each single angel is terrible.* No. So he is an angel.

Roger would be the one at the station.

2

Fifteen minutes later she was still lying there on the bed, staring vacantly up at the ceiling, when she heard steps on the stairs. Not Mrs. Josiah's weasel ones and not Mr. Josiah's bullish ones. Her blood iced. She sat bolt up. The door was closed but it was not locked. Blind panic gripped her. These were not Carrie Hibbard's steady, irreducible steps. And, of course, they stopped on the other side of her door! Had she supposed Brother Boyd and his friends (that "pretty rough bunch"—Seth Erwin's warning words!) were going to let her leave town without paying their respects?

There—there was the knock.

She combed her hair with her fingers, smoothed her dress. The knock came again. She stood up and faced the door.

"You may come in," was the way she put it.

It was William Morrison.

Staring at him, at his solid wooden figure, she backed off a little. He looked sightlessly around the room, his eyes coming slightly alive only when he spotted her bags.

"I'm not leaving till five o'clock," she said. "Sit down, William Morrison."

He sat down on the straight chair, she on the edge of the bed. If he was playing hooky, she decided that was his business. She found herself remembering how, as stiff as a wooden soldier, he had found it necessary to erase everything off the boards—he was just as stiff, just as dogged and literal in his grief, sitting in the straight chair now. He had not allowed her to provide him with an opening then and he would not now. She could only wait. She took a cigarette from her purse, which was within reach, and lighted it. He had lost his friend to an enemy he could not boss; he was losing her, though he had formed that committee to prevent it. And it was with a start she realized that as chairman of that same committee set up in opposition to his father, he might also have lost his esteem for his father (lost his father) as another part of the price. Odd, she thought, his blaming his father, as she did, for her leaving; perhaps thinking it un-forgivable. But if he *knew?* Knew the thoughts she had been entertaining, lying on a bed, before he came in? Who would it then be he could never forgive? His father? *And* his teacher? Regarding him through the smoke of her cigarette, she knew the sheer weight of hopelessness. As William Morrison's teacher she too would have to renounce (would have had to renounce had she been given the chance). If Seth Erwin could not go with her to the ends of the earth for being so trapped as Seth the son of Zebulon in Peegram, neither could she have gone with him for being his son's teacher. Daring all else, she still could not, would not dare that. It would have meant a guilt which would consume love and which she never could have surmounted. . . . This literal, dogged quality of his grief. She had had an uncle, her mother's brother, who had died of cancer of the lungs at home on the farm rather than at the hospital. When her uncle breathed his tortured last, her uncle's dog lay down on the front porch and never got up again, never took food or water again. While keeping both food and water within his reach, her aunt would not let anybody try to move the dog. "Let him be," she said. In not very many days, the dog was dead, her aunt burying him behind the hedge, spading the grave herself and watering it with the tears she had not been able to shed till then.

She should not be leaving William Morrison now, she thought in her despair—he needed her so. With that capacity for loving of his which had from the first alarmed her! Among her children, Ray and William Morrison were the ones dearest to her heart, the ones she loved most. But Ray, caught up in his dream, had not been in a position to love anybody outside its boundaries. Ray had not of course loved her, and if he had, she might have gotten through to him, except as then he should not have required "getting through to." Ray had been far, far too sick with lovelessness for loving. William Morrison was the one who loved her. It was not right, leaving him, at this time, and when his grief was in its critical phase; it was deeply wrong.

"Miss L . . ."

"Yes," she said.

"That day."

"Yes, William Morrison." (There was only one day and there might be only one day, with all its ramifications, hereafter, forever.)

"You said . . . you started out . . . about his dad . . . but you didn't . . ."

(Ah, then. The day after the day, a ramification.) She said, "I couldn't. I mean, I didn't think . . ."

"Yeah. We stopped you—they did, me too, but . . . Look, we didn't never talk about him. Didn't think you should. Thought you done wrong to try."

"Why, William Morrison?"

He looked at her. "Don't you know?"

"No."

He frowned. "But everybody knows."

"In this town, I'm not 'everybody.'"

"He took up with a Negra. He tried to sell him some land or something, I don't know much about all that, but it was what turned 'em all against him. And what did he do? He killed hisself. Took and drowned hisself in the river."

Yes, she thought, rebellion, defeat. *Liberty and justice for all, black and white.* She had known.

"We thought he was yellow, Miss L. Me too. Some old droopy-drawers, who'd care?—But *him*! We thought he was the scum for doing what he done. Why, he was a—a—"

"A hero?"

"Yes'm. He was a hero, football, baseball, ace pilot in the war. He could catch more fish and shoot better than . . . *Him* yellow."

"But—"

He waved her down with one decisive gesture of his hand (which, despite the gesture certainly all its own, was re- markably like his father's hand, narrow and tapered, a re- semblance she had not noticed till now).

"Go on," she murmured. (And what was she trying to do —compete with his mother whom she would have dismissed as "pristine"?) She added, "And don't say 'hisself' and 'we didn't never' and 'done what he done'—how many times have I told you?"

"It don't matter now," he said.

(And of course she let the "it don't" pass. He was playing hooky in more ways than one; in more ways than one letting her know he could not bear to see her go. He always spoke ungrammatically—out of reaction to his overrefined father and mother, she supposed—but he could do better than he was doing now.)

"Did Ray know all this?" she asked.

"About a thousand ways."

Their eyes met.

"That day," William Morrison said, "right before the game, he stood up and yelled his dad's name out."

"Yes," she said, probing with the mercilessness love so often requires. "And you wouldn't let him yell it out, would you?"

"No, we wouldn't!"

"Go on, William Morrison."

"Well . . . I was sittin' with him at the game."

There was a long, long pause. Martha had to put out her cigarette which would have burned her fingers had she not.

"Right next to him. Same bench."

"Same bench." (Like a refrain that needs to be repeated after every verse.)

"They say Ray got all flustered and mixed up. They say he didn't know what he was doin' when the ball come his way—didn't see it till it was on him. I know different, Miss L. I yelled at him in plenty of time. Ray saw the ball."

William Morrison stood up. " 'Stead of duckin', this is what he done. He stood up quick and his arms come out like this." William Morrison raised his arms up and out from his sides. "You see, Miss L?"

He dropped his arms and sat down. "Fred, he saw enough to make him cryin' mad, but Fred he didn't see all I seen. It was like he was ready and waitin' for it, Miss L. It was like *he* . . . killed *hisself*. He yelled it out about bein' like his dad and then . . ."

"Maybe we don't know enough about it," Martha said lamely.

"*I* know," William Morrison said. "*I* know and you gotta know, same as me."

Their eyes meeting again.

"You call what Ray did yellow, Miss L?"

"No," she said without the slightest trace of hesitation.

"What do you call it, Miss L?"

"I call it only very very sad, that he had to want it that way, if he did."

William Morrison said, "I call it . . . I . . . Miss L, now I'm not even right sure his dad was yellow, not any more, not now. *We* done it to Ray, Miss L, you said so. And—"

"No, I didn't, William Morrison. I didn't mean it like that. I— You never could have known a foul ball was going to—"

But he waved her down. "It was wantin' it that made it come true, Miss L. We done it to Ray by makin' him want it—oh, I've been thinkin' plenty. And if we done it to Ray, did folks do it to his dad too? Why, Miss L? *Why?* And . . . Now, what? What do we do now?"

His face was suddenly red and contorted, his breast was heaving. He was not a child who cried easily. He nearly dug his eyes out with his fists.

And now what indeed were they going to do, when she was leaving in a matter of hours? But the tears were good, very good, if only . . .

She decided she would take a terrible chance, because there was no other way. When his crying had abated, she said, "William Morrison. I think you had better take all this up with your dad."

William Morrison leaped to his feet, upsetting the chair. "*My* dad? Are you crazy, Miss L?"

"No," she said, also standing up.

"You don't know nothin' about my dad, you don't know him."

"Yes, I do."

"No, ma'am, you don't. You rode in the car with him one time. *My* dad." He laughed and it was not a pretty sound. "You forget *my* dad fired you, Miss L? That's not all. *My* dad and *his* dad were pals, roommates in college and all that. But if you think my dad helped his dad when everybody turned on him in that Negra business—well, I said I didn't know nothin' about it, but I know this much—I know he never did."

"I admire your dad," she said evenly.

The chance taken, the chance that she would disillusion him completely. But unless Seth Erwin could help his son affirm life, at this juncture, it was a tragedy that would go on and on, generation after generation, and who knew when it would ever stop?

"Why aren't you named Zebulon, William Morrison?" (She could not have been more surprised at her own question; or, for that matter, more shocked at her timing of it. Seth the son of Zebulon the son of Seth, generation upon generation, when here was William Morrison. She might at least have posed the question to herself before putting it to him!)

"Who cares?" William Morrison muttered.

"I tell you," she said, looking at her watch, taking still another chance inasmuch as she knew very well she ought never to encounter Seth Erwin again for her own sake. "I tell

you, William Morrison. I believe I'm going to have a talk
with your father myself. I've just about got time. Where
would I find him—at home or at the church?"

"At the church," William Morrison muttered, shuffling his
feet, ramming his fists into his pockets.

But it was all right—she could see that darkly, dubiously,
it was all right with him for her to go to see his father. He
gave her his dark and doubtful and dubious permission.

She covered the distance between them in one step and
lifted the square chin in her hand. She looked into his eyes—
a look that he returned. Quickly, she planted a kiss on his
forehead.

" 'By, Miss L."

"Good-by, William Morrison."

3

Glancing furtively right and left, and back over her shoulder
as well, she hastened through the streets. She was sure she
was being followed. She should have taken a cab, she told
herself. There were such things as cabs in Peegram!

In turning a corner, she nearly collided with a tall, heavy-
set man, also hastening, whom she would have mistaken for
white were it not for the small black boy at his side. The
man stared at her, his lips came open, he seemed on the
point of speaking, but instead he smiled a strange stiff smile
and took the child's hand. Not the face or the smile—they
repelled her—but his gesture, the way he had very nearly
introduced the child and her, appealed—she nodded to them
and hastened on. Had she seen them some place before?

He stood up slowly, coming around from behind his desk, blinking his eyes, as if against too strong a light.

Was it that he had been in a dream of her?

"I told you I didn't want you to leave the rooming house."

She turned abruptly away from him and, to control herself, she began to walk about his study, staring at the books on his book shelves, with their titles all alike, *The Light of Faith, Man's Great Adventure with Faith, The Modern Battle for Faith, The Inner Light, The Gospel of Modern Thought, A Guide to Confident Living, The New Quest for Salvation,* etcetera, etcetera, etcetera. She supposed there must be others, some properly forbidding and dreary tomes (in sets, with expensive bindings) and still others, like Dewey, or Whitehead, or Hobbs, or Hume, which she couldn't see, for the company they kept. How shabby of him. You didn't know a man until you knew him in his work. As if he could play nothing straight. As if literature and truth were the sin poor Peegram was to be everlastingly forbidden, or could never be expected to condone. What a tower of strength he was. How intricately insulting. You did not blame people who worshiped counterfeits and copies when they had never encountered the originals and knew no better—but him! If she had not made her promise to William Morrison, she told herself, she would have left without a word.

But she turned to him. "I've just come from your son. In the first place, I'd like to know why you named him William Morrison instead of Zebulon."

His eyes grew slowly cold; his poise was in no way disturbed. Neither did he deign to answer her.

She returned her attention to this study of his which she

had never been in. It was subtly expensive in all its appointments and furnishings. Except for a rather battered walnut-framed mirror, which seemed out of character, everything bespoke excellent taste and a bank account. The inlaid, hand-tooled desk was a thing of beauty, there was no question, yet so discreet that unless you had money or certain leanings, you would probably not have given it a second look. Everything—drapes, carpet, pictures—had that stamp. And she would have thrown everything away! It was so damn correct that it made her long for a bearskin rug and orange crates, painted red. Out of the corner of her eye, she saw that he had moved back behind his desk. She turned to him again.

"You wouldn't tell me about Harry Hibbard."

But, there. That did strike home, as she had known it would. He was groping for his chair, sinking into it and sitting there, flexing his hands in a peculiar way she had not previously observed in him.

"William Morrison is the one who has told me," she went on. "He's told me enough for me to be able to fit a good many pieces together."

"Good," he said quietly. "You were so sure you had the right to know. . . . Harry Hibbard was my friend. Like you, he had his troubles around the race issue."

"And you let him down just as you have let me down."

"Far worse than that."

"So? You and Carrie Hibbard fired me. Did you and Carrie 'fire' him too? Is that it?"

"That . . . describes it fairly adequately."

"I see."

"*Do* you?"

There was a pause. She could not stand it and did not

think that he could. Grief and rage made the room seem to spin drunkenly.

"Did you see Ray get hit?" she finally asked, remembering by an effort of will why she was here.

"Not many people saw that. The sun was going down and it was the way the sun was shining—directly into most of our eyes. But . . . all right . . . you shall know: at the critical moment I closed my eyes."

She didn't trust her voice to match his for quietness and did not say, "So like you."

His hands flexed. "I . . . think I was trying to pray."

Her heart contracted. The room spun. She could not say anything at all for she didn't know how long, wanting so to take him in her arms. Somehow she knew it was the first time he had ever revealed himself to another.

"Your son did see," she said. "He was sitting with Ray and he saw everything. He says Ray stood up to greet the ball. Instead of ducking. He says Ray killed himself as his father did before him. He says his brother Fred knows this too, or strongly suspects it."

In broken, jerky phrases, she told him of what had transpired in the schoolroom before Ray went to the game. She told him it was very nearly the last thing he said, "liberty and justice for all, black and white," and "I'll be like my dad." He listened so absolutely that her burden felt lightened.

When she was through, he said, "I have a hunch—it seems too ironical now—but I have a very substantial hunch that Harry came home, most of all, to save this particular son."

". . . Seth." (It was a slip, but he had called her Martha once.)

"Yes."

"Are you going to save *your* son?"

He looked at her, hating her of course. She should never have spoken those words so tenderly.

"You and Harry Hibbard were friends," she said, stumbling on. "What about Ray and William Morrison? And there's blood between them too. He's lost Ray for some reasons that aren't very pretty and that he's not dodging. And he's losing me—he loves me, incidentally. The way he sees it, you're responsible for firing me—didn't he fight you on it? The way he sees it, your hands aren't clean in regard to Harry Hibbard's death either. And that death brought on Ray's, which he's taken on himself and the other children in the room. He's having to ask his questions very young. One is, *Why?* He's learning—God knows, too fast—about hate and unreason and death. And now it follows—he's got to ask with everything he has, What's life about? I don't know what you can do about it—it seems improbable and fantastic but all of it has turned around the race issue, if that's any hint—but I do know that if you don't do something, he's kaput—finished, and he won't kill himself, he'll live his death, likely for a very long time. He's built strong."

"We're not close," Seth Erwin muttered, apparently incapable of looking at her. "We don't talk the same language. What can I do?"

"What do you take me for?" she said. "Don't you know I'm aware that you think you hate him—or just about that—and that he is quite sure he hates you? I told you, I didn't have an idea what you could do, but you have to do something!"

He stood up, went to the window and stared out.

"If you don't," she said, "he'll destroy himself working as hard to be *unlike* you as ever Ray did, working so hard to be *like* Harry Hibbard."

He stood motionless.

"Your son's only a great man in embryo, that's all. Born to his times. With a genius that's political."

Motionless. The statue of a man, merely. *You won't mind that what I think is you're a hypocrite and a coward, will you?* Her eyes misted. "I told William Morrison that I admire you."

He turned slowly. "William Morrison is not the only one who loves you," he said.

"Fathers and sons," she said sadly, sardonically. "I've heard it often happens."

They looked at each other.

"My bus leaves at five."

Looked at her watch: ten minutes past four. All her rage that she had thought dispelled intact, she discovered.

"You can say it now," she said. "You have me safely on my way. Out of reach. Beyond temptation. 'The general situation!' I ought to laugh and laugh. It's you that makes my leaving so essential. Well, I'm going."

"Tell me. Could you still say what you've just said if you knew you might be resting in a hospital today, or a cemetery, if I hadn't 'stooped' to discourage Brother Boyd Saturday?"

She smiled mysteriously, perversely. "I thought there must have been something of that sort."

Had she?

He made a sudden move toward her. Maybe he would have hit her, or laid his hands on both her shoulders, or enfolded her in his arms, or crushed her to him—the power and the glory to possess her utterly—but she would never know, she moved so swiftly away.

"You do something about William Morrison!" she said, making for the door.

"I'm driving you back."

"You're never driving me anywhere again." She groped for the door knob through her tears. "What have I got out of this, Seth Erwin? I've lost my first job—do you know what that means? I have to leave my children when they need me most. Maybe I'll have to leave the state—it's the nearest thing to home I've ever known. And I have to leave you— lose you—yes, you might as well know it for the record—I love you too."

"Martha!"

"No!" she cried, jerking the door open. "The least you can do is—it's all I ask of you—save your son."

She slammed the door behind her and ran.

4

Roger waved good-by to her from the station platform, his martyred face going on and on, after the bus had made its turn, because he was bald. Peegram, she saw, was a bird sanctuary. It said so on the city limits sign they had already left behind.

Seth Erwin

1

WHEN, ORDINARILY, MONDAY BUSINESS WAS FAIRLY BRISK, IT was so deserted and so quiet in his church study the Monday morning three weeks to the day after Martha Lyerly had taken her departure that when the telephone rang, he was startled. It rang a second time before he got his bearings. "Short" Mitchel was the party on the other end of the line. Short was a crony of his father's in the old days, about the same age his father would be if his father were living. Since Short owned Mitchel's Funeral Home, the one favored by Baptists in Peegram, he and Seth necessarily had their dealings. Short treated Seth in the condescending, familiar way he thought proper to the son whose father he had been on such intimate terms with. (Seth's father and Short had founded the Spittoon Club.) Short liked to ask Seth how he was making out at shooting craps or to pretend he had seen him at the last cock fight he had attended. He always greeted Seth with a lascivious wink. And when he was in his cups, he was apt to tell you about what he did to women's corpses. At best, Seth could not abide him.

"Seth, old boy," Short said now, hawking his throat, "just had a call I thought you might want to hear about. Somebody wantin' to know if Jim's body had come in yet. Know what I told him? Told him we didn't dirty our hands on dead niggers at Mitchel's, no sir. Told him to call Ebony Funeral Service, *they'd* know. Those were my exact words, Seth, old boy. But guess what he wanted to know next crack out of the bag?"

He waited greedily for Seth to ask what, but went on when Seth did not.

"He wanted to know about yours, Seth, old boy. Wanted to know had *it* come in yet."

"And what did you tell him?" Seth asked, replacing the receiver so noiselessly that Short might even suppose something had gone wrong with their connection.

He sat back and locked his hands behind his head. So that was how the Silence Treatment was broken. What did he expect after that epileptic seizure of his yesterday? Yesterday, he, Seth Erwin, pastor of the First Baptist Church of Peegram, had preached a full-dress sermon on the topic of, and in favor of, desegregation and integration. This he had not intended to do, he was in no way forewarned. Proved by the fact that there was not one mention of desegregation in the sermon notes he had prepared so carefully in advance and no hint of it in the church bulletin in which the sermon title had been printed up as "Solitude and Self-Realization."

It was the more awkward in that it was only on May the thirty-first, the Tuesday before this Sunday, that the momentous news of the outcome of the Supreme Court's review had hit the nation, and the state, and Peegram. The last hope that the Court would back down gone. Had he had any inkling of what he was about, he would certainly have waited for the first wave of anger to subside. Or he could have fizzled. He could for once have seen to it, in his unconscious, that his golden eloquence let him down. As it was, his sermon had been inspired—terrific—superb. He had very little memory of its particulars, but he had the strong suspicion that it was one of his best. As the final twist of the knife, here he was, doubtless about to be crucified for his stand, when in point of fact he did not believe in that stand which he had now so irrevocably and publicly proclaimed! If there was any-thing fitting and appropriate about this state of affairs, he confessed he failed to see it. The one lone redeeming feature was that he did know, this time, beyond being blind with hate and revulsion, who Jim was. This meant he could vi-brate more quiveringly to the blows as they fell, though per-haps without ceasing to wonder why Jim had to be here.

What was Jim up to? It occurred to him that he might ask. That it might have some slight bearing on "the general situation."

He glanced around his study.

The Supreme Court had held "that local school authorities must act in good faith to implement the constitutional princi-ples declared in the 1954 decision." The "go slow but go." And now, the State Legislature's resolution, adopted in April, met it hard-on: "The mixing of the races in the public schools cannot be accomplished." The General Assembly's assignment statute loomed too (with its real meaning tucked quietly away). Ostensibly, this statute removed race as a factor in the assignment of students and empowered local unit school boards to admit students on the basis of *health* and *welfare* and *other factors*. Oh, you could see it now! And there was a question: what local school program bearing the label of integration or desegregation could get an appropriation from the Legislature, which still held and would continue to hold the purse strings? And there was an answer: not one.

"Lawful avoidance"—that was a lovely phrase. Well, but the Court had moved in and upset its own precedent of fifty-eight years' standing. There would be "voluntary segregation," in which the Negroes would be asked to give up their constitutional rights voluntarily—and anybody could define "voluntarily" who wanted to. There would be boycotting of businesses, all sorts of quiet and insidious economic pressure. Could the Court *operate* the schools—or the city busses, or the playgrounds, or the golf courses; because it wasn't just schools but all Jim Crow which was in the balance, of course, and with the schools only the beginning. But the public schools could die before the Court's ruling should become law! Let there be private schools (for the children of factory workers and tenant farmers). What a mess it would be, and what a paradox if education was what would be sacrificed.

There would be citizens' councils, state's rights councils, defenders of state sovereignty, and the Lord knew what. Incidents and more incidents. Governors' conferences and special sessions of legislatures. Petitions and counter-petitions. Resolutions of protest, campaigns to amend the Constitution, maybe even that old doctrine of interposition dug up. Speeches. Reams upon reams of editorials. (He sighed to think of all the editorials and letters-to-the-editor that would be written.)

And then where were you, after the tumult and the shouting? Not back where you started from. But, in one stroke, the quite considerable progress of over half a century was canceled. You could not overturn a whole tradition and a whole heritage. The Court's way was not only not the right way but the way of retrenchment and regression and grievous trouble; tragedy. Good God, hadn't they proved that in Peegram?

So, knowing which to the very marrow of his bones, Seth Erwin had to preach his sermon! At just about the exact same moment in time when a gentleman from Mississippi was letting his voice be heard: "The effect of the Supreme Court decision is to open the bedroom door of every white woman in the South to a Negro."

And had he, truly, let one immigrant laborer's daughter push him into this? (Yes, he was a snob!) One he would never even see again, let alone . . . ?

And didn't he *know* about the incest nightmare, and the passing of those, like Aunt Phoebe and Aunt Deb, with the intricate blood knowledge? Didn't he have good reason to know it was the white man who, if anything, had rather kept his foot in the Negro woman's bedroom door? He shuddered. If the Court did not understand guilt and the wages of guilt, he did. If the Court ignored the recency of the Civil War and all the revival of interest in it, he did not. He remembered a verse from a song of the '70s Aunt Phoebe and Aunt Deb had used to sing to him:

I hate the Constitution, this great Republic too;
I hate the nasty eagle and the uniform so blue.
I hate their glorious banner and all their flags and fuss:
Those thievin' lyin' Yankees, I hate 'em wuss and wuss.

The Court would have done far better to have taken its lesson from Aunt Phoebe and Aunt Deb rather than from sociologists. During World War II, Peegram came down with a fit of patriotism, in no small part brought on by the news stories of its hero, Harry Hibbard. It decided to fly the Stars and Stripes over the courthouse for the first time. Accordingly, a flag was bought, concrete was poured and the pole was set. (The "other" pole for the "other" flag had rotted out.) But the ceremonies of flag raising had no sooner got under way, with the Boy Scouts and Air Raid Wardens much in evidence, than Aunt Phoebe and Aunt Deb put in their appearance. They made a speech, each. They said this sacrilege could not be tolerated. They shook their umbrellas at the Boy Scouts. Not only did the Stars and Stripes not fly that day but never did until well after the moony night Aunt Phoebe and Aunt Deb consigned themselves to the flames.

. . . The sons of Ham. Martha Lyerly might suppose her stand was the only one a Christian could take! He could give her chapter and verse: "Our Creator segregated man. Had He not intended to segregate man, we would all be the same color. Therefore, it is against the will of our Creator to abolish segregation and God is on our side." Q.E.D. Then there was always the extension of the same argument with its undercurrent confusion, species-wise, between the Negroes and the apes. He set this sort of thing against the Court and the

NAACP sort of thing, and his wish to wash his hands of the
whole business became acute. Each side was more strident
and more foolish than the other. Nor could he help it that
when he tried to envisage a heritage of jungle and slavery,
his entire being cringed.

Why not, much better, bring the atom bomb into his pulpit? "All atomic fission must be immediately halted under
international law, or mankind (segregated or unsegregated)
and all other forms of life must disappear from the earth,
though there be no atomic war."—There. And he could air
his fanciful notion, that this wasn't the first atomic age but
was probably what was the matter with the other planets
and stars upon which there was no life; that there had been
many atomic ages in the great experiment God had flung out;
and that the youngster who had told him to pray for God
was right.

He unlocked his hands from behind his head. It was certainly a silent study this Monday morning.

2

These past three weeks. When he could not come near the
study, or else rushed to it, to play it through again, where she
had stood and what she had said and what he had said. For
three weeks wrapped in cotton wool, yet bleeding. He did
not ask how Elaine had stood his raw nerves and edginess—
she was made to stand anything and everything, except the
one thing he had now done to her in preaching his sermon.
It would have been so much better, he had told himself over
and over, if he had fallen in love when he was very young;

had some experience of it; some premonition of what was in store for him. At least he would have guarded better against the fantasies—when they were bright, or broken, or simply weary and vague, or jagged and bitter, but always on and on and on. Each day, each night rising to its crisis: he would fling everything away and go after her. But he always returned to the same bitter truth—loving him, she would never have him, because of her concern for his son. Oh, she had made that abundantly clear. Then—and maybe this was yet more bitter, though it seldom figured in the fantasies—his realization that it did not matter because he could never really leave, regardless. So that if there was an end of the line, it was the end of the line of his life. Of Peegram. Of everything.

If she had pushed him toward his sermon, it was also to escape her that he had preached it. And he would say that for all the Silence Treatment since yesterday and for all his own astonishment and anger with himself, it was still better than what had been going on in him for three weeks—it was more firm, more real. And he would say that he could at least now locate some thoughts in his mind that were not about her and that did not, no matter what, paint her mouth and the lights in her hair and the turn of her head and the round of her breasts, and, and, and. *And* that the dead weight of his guilt around his dead friend was easier? Yes, that was also true. And true, that it kept returning, the one splintered thought of William Morrison, broadside before his sermon, listening to his sermon.

What was he going to do? Sit here? (And now that the undertaker had broken the Silence Treatment?) Were there not steps he should take? Possibilities he should consider?

Decisions to be arrived at? For instance, there was a regularly scheduled board of deacons meeting tomorrow. Carrie was not on his board of deacons (generally, Baptists do not go in for deaconesses)—he knew very well she did not need to be. Except in her pew Sundays, he had not seen Carrie since Ray's death. Carrie had been in her pew yesterday. He had not looked to see whether that polite state of sleep his sermons customarily put her in was disturbed—he had not needed to, had he? (*You fight her, Seth, you're left.*)

Was his sermon to be followed by others—was that it? Was he going to "plug away" for integration, not believing; never believing; God had not given him faith. And were sermons (supposing *they* should be made somehow to allow them) were sermons to be the sum of his . . . of his . . . fight? (Ah, Harry, Harry, Harry.)

But instead of pushing on ahead and "arriving," he found himself looking back; recalling one of his old professors at the seminary he had not thought of in years. Old Mackie. Old Mackie was no free spirit, he was erratic and sloppy and wrong and unsystematic (theologically speaking) and he was scorned by students and colleagues alike. He clacked his false teeth and he picked his nose, sometimes in public—he was a terrible and inexcusable old man. Seth took only one course under him. He finally got kicked out, but that was not in Seth's day.

"Ye worship ye know not what" was Old Mackie's theme. At least once a week he would proclaim, "The church may be no more than organized opposition to man's true religious impulse." He liked to contend that the masochistic solution to the sadistic impulse had failed. Turn the other cheek, walk the second mile, had failed. Loving one's enemies had failed. Learn about hate before it's too late, he was forever saying— explore it, the whole realm of the unconscious is now before us; stop pushing it down and out; stop unloading it on poor old Satan and his counterparts. God is Love and Hate, he would say, shocking most of them speechless, but usually following such a pronouncement with some such question as, "Why should there be, upon men, at all times, everywhere, some pressure to find 'the truth' and 'create the beautiful,' if the universe were indifferent to these values?"

Seth had agreed with the others that Old Mackie was off his rocker, but he had listened to him with the aching intentness that he had never brought to the others.

The resemblance between Old Mackie and Seth's father had not occurred to him till now, after all these years. Curious.

And all their eyes still fixed, hoping to find once more,
Being by Calvary's turbulence unsatisfied,
The uncontrollable mystery on the bestial floor.

He stirred. That sermon of his. He wished he could re-member something about it, but all he could remember was that he had quoted, "For it pleased God by the foolishness of preaching to save them that believe." He rather liked that, "the foolishness of preaching" and the saving of "them that believe." Pascal's having the Lord say, "Comfort yourself, you would not seek me if you had not found me." (Not in his sermon, this last.)

What now? The study, gathering silence.

3

It was Jim, and Jimbo, who interrupted the silence of the study. (He taking a hasty—and needed—glance in the walnut-framed mirror! No dandruff, but . . .)

"I'm sorry, I didn't have any place I much wanted to leave him," Jim said, indicating Jimbo.

Seth stood up and, from his book shelves, reached for the picture books and the Pogo and the Little Lulu comics he kept on hand for the children whose mothers came to unburden themselves of their sins and who had no place to leave their children behind. He handed these to Jim (rather than Jimbo). Jim installed Jimbo in a chair by the window, without issuing the customary warning of mothers, "Now, you be careful of these, you hear? You remember they don't belong to you."

At first, Seth felt rather inclined to be bored. This was his half-brother-in-the-blood, their moment of meeting (for it was indeed their moment of meeting) and, no doubt, as he said to himself, it should be a moment pregnant and dripping with drama, which being so, it was difficult for him to overcome his own disposition to withdraw. At least Jimbo was lost, was entranced with the picture books and the comics; obviously, he was beginning at the top and was going to work down. He was so little, in the vast chair that Jim had put him in, that he could not bend his knees, so that his legs stuck straight out. Regarding Jim (who was regarding him), Seth saw that the pale, puffy face (the putty face which, as he had previously noted, so obligingly offered itself to the hostile imagination as the happiest possible material for dents) had in fact undergone alterations. The end of the nose was skinned; there was a cut which rather followed the contours of the left half of the mouth, looking almost as if someone might have lifted the face and then, with deliberate care, used a knife rather than a lipstick to outline an extra mouth and had got only half done when there was an interruption of some sort. It was a cut that had obviously had several stitches taken in it and was pulling the putty face into a new alignment. One tooth—perhaps two—were missing. The way he held his mouth, it was hard to tell. The conventional opening to conversation they might have found was hindered in that Seth could not keep his eyes from straying to this cut; further hindered in that, clearly, Jim was not going to *call* Seth anything, and Seth, as he understood, was forbidden to call Jim Jim. The ambiguous "you" was going to have to stand for a great deal. Their silence was long and stubborn and only disturbed by Jimbo turning the pages of his picture book.

When Seth could stand it no longer, he said, "How did it happen? How did you get the cut?"

"About a week ago," Jim said. "In the courthouse square. I was stooping over the water fountain for a drink of water and got shoved into it by some white men who came up from behind."

"But you aren't supposed to use that fountain, are you?" Seth said. "Where there are not two fountains, one expressly designated as 'Colored,' it is understood, isn't it, that colored people don't drink?"

They looked at each other.

"The news of your sermon has traveled fast," Jim said.

"Is that so?"

Jim's look slipped off Seth, going to Jimbo and the window, on the other side of which were the neat green grass and the well-trimmed maples.

"I was all set in Madison," he said. "I had a good job, good place to live. I was getting on."

Jim's voice was bitter, if controlled. Seth—since he himself had had to come back to Peegram too—did not dispute the bitter Erwin necessity. He felt it was fate, but it was nevertheless bitterly that he said, "So you had to come back here!"

"Yes."

"And what makes you suppose—(his eyes reviewed the cut again)—that Andy Boyd and his bunch are going to let you alone? Or your boy alone? What are you about? And what kind of job have you been able to shake down—just incidentally?"

"I have an organization behind me," Jim said. "I have been sent back here by that organization for a purpose. And while, so far, I've been lying fairly low, I won't be 'encouraged' out of town this time."

Jim's look veered from the window back to Seth; their look hung fire. Seth wanted to laugh; he wanted to say, "You can serve your organization dead as well as alive, I trust?"

Jim fairly lifted this thought out of his mind by saying, "As a martyr, I should be followed by, who knows, a hundred more that I may be able to inspire with circumstances as they are, so I can't be made afraid. Not on my own account and not on the boy's. There is too much at stake for his future and the future of all the boys like him. You could not be expected to believe it, when he's so very young, but he and I understand each other in this. . . . From what I have heard of what he said on the subject of folks and dogs, another son understood his father too."

Making no reply, Seth stared at the cut that repeated the contours of half a mouth, referring his impression of it to the deeper recesses of his mind where it would no doubt make a putty of its own.

"And you asked me about jobs," Jim said. "As a matter of fact, that's why I've come to you today. I've come to offer you my services."

"So?" (But as if his own mouth were the wound.)

"You may not have been apprised of it yet—I only just got the news myself—but your church janitor has quit his job as of this morning."

"No," Seth said, "I have not been *apprised* of that."

"Alonzo Jennings, your janitor, is one of those who desert a sinking ship most promptly. The kind who can be trusted to get out of trouble before trouble starts. As you know, I have had considerable janitorial experience, and I am here to offer you my services."

(Yes, Seth thought: Seth Erwin, Pastor; James Erwin, Janitor. It would look so cozy on the books; it would so please the deacons and the membership; such a perfect postscript to the sermon just preached. Still, who had helped fire whom from what janitor's job? This subtlety in revenge should not go unappreciated; it was exquisitely fitting and exquisitely timed. "Considerable janitorial experience" on the part of the one whose working vocabulary included words like "apprised.")

"I don't have anything to do with it," Seth muttered. "It goes through the Building and Grounds committee."

"But you could recommend me to that committee, couldn't

you? You could put my name up? You see, my organization is not an organization of unlimited funds. I need work, I have to have it. And the janitor's salary of $2,400 that your church offers—making it very nearly the highest-paid job for a person of my race in this town—would go far to helping our cause."

Seth said, "I don't want you to think I don't appreciate the —uh—beauty of your coming to me here to 'offer your services,' but in the plain light of day, I can't believe Alonzo has quit. He wouldn't have quit simply because . . ." His voice trailed off.

"I beg your pardon," Jim said, "but Mr. Jennings *has* quit. He has been apprised of developments involving your church that are yet to come, and he does not care to be connected with it in any capacity. Mr. Jennings is, of course, a coward."

Seth waited.

Jim smiled thinly, on one side of his mouth. He said, "It seems that several members of the colored church—Emmanuel Baptist—are so impressed by what they have heard of your sermon that they are planning to come to your church here, this next Sunday, and worship with you."

Seth stood up. "And this is your idea." He did not ask, he did not need to ask.

"I'm not a member of the Emmanuel Church myself," Jim said. But added, "Yes, it is my idea. I thought of it."

Seth was pacing the study.

"I thought it would give your sermon more . . . reference."

"But why didn't you wait for Communion Sunday? Isn't that an oversight? The riot would have more . . . reference."

He walked up and down. Short Mitchel and the party

wanting to know if Jim's body had come in yet; if his had. . . . When you came down to it, was each so greedy for the crucifixion? How the silence in the study had gathered; how he had waited. Well this *was* the end.

Suddenly, he turned on Jim. "I thought you were for your race!" He could have bitten his tongue out, and he could not then go on and add, "All right, all right, you mongrel, I take it back."

"I think we might try to understand each other to this extent," Jim was saying quietly. "I had a friend and I have a son—this is a larger matter with me than personal revenge. I needed a job, this opportunity offered, I came to you. That wasn't so easy for me to do. But I've been a janitor all my life and I'm not too proud to be a janitor the rest of my life, it's the boy I ask more of the future for. I have been sent back here by the organization we spoke of to start a test case in the courts with regard to my boy's Constitutional right to enter a decent school this fall. I could have done this in Madison. But there are others in Madison who are ready and willing to do it, whereas no one was ready and willing here. And in view of my friend's and my unfinished business here, as you might say, I felt there was nothing else I could do but return. It is our intention to spearhead this same sort of thing all over the state and the South. This is the time. We have to put things to the test now. Peegram is not the nation and the nation is going to back us up now. We're not as helpless as we were. If we strike now, we may win. Your sermon offers us another opportunity to put things to the test, that's all."

Seth sat down. "But don't you *see* . . . ?" he said. "Look," he said. "You and *your* friend didn't win your way. You know you didn't! So you come back to try more of the same. Why not fight it smart this time? What's so wrong with that? Why not give yourself one slender chance to win?"

They eyed each other in silence for a moment. Jim said, "It seems to me that one of the main reasons my friend and I didn't win was because some one or two worked very hard seeing to it that we couldn't. After your sermon, I . . ."

(You came to plead! You came with the dawn of new hope in your heart. Ah, how different is each man's perspective. Here I thought he had come only to lay me on the griddle and watch me writhe. But all the same, so much hate getting in the way. How on earth can either of us be expected to get a grip on his hate?) He was breathing in a quick, shallow fashion; staring at his hands. "Why don't you try fighting it my way?" he asked.

Silence. *His* way. And other than sermons, what was his way then? He looked almost shyly at Jim. "I'm the one who stopped Andy Boyd," he said.

"That's true," Jim said. "With words. Good enough in that case, since they held off action. But it's action of our own we're after. You stopped him and you relayed a message to me not to come to the graveside service. I don't subscribe to *your* way. I only ask that you don't hinder ours this time, if your sermon is a sign that—you have your regrets. I did not stay away from the graveside out of any giving in to your way. It was merely that I didn't wish to take the chance of inciting them further, when the schoolteacher . . . I hadn't realized . . ."

"Exactly," Seth said, putting away the pain and the quick thrust of pleasure the reference to Martha Lyerly brought

him, along with the temptation to engage Jim in a long conversation about her in which all his own reactions would be
his secret.

But Jim was looking at him measuringly. "The schoolteacher is out of the way now, with you to thank. What *is*
your way? I confess I'd like to hear your own description
of it."

Seth studied his hands; they were hands that pleased him
every whit as much as his face did. They were hands that
reminded him of Mozart's music; they were the fine and intricate work of centuries. He looked up—gazed upon the
scarred and puffy face, considered in imagination the body-
heaviness with which this one sat waiting for Seth Erwin to
reveal himself. No memory of a small boy on the other side
of a thorn hedge intruded; it was the detached and floating
memory of a fat, black face with its mouth open; of jelly-like
buttocks that shook and shook.

"It's keeping those colored worshipers out of my church,
for one thing!"

Seth had flicked it out. Jim nodded. His eyes said, "Naturally."

Seth said, "It's not letting you have the church janitor's
job."

Jim said, "Of course."

"Damnation!" Seth said. He opened and shut his hands
(his beautiful hands which by every right and reason ought
to stay clean). Jim was not breaking this silence. Seth's shallow breathing subsided. "It's tilling the soil before you plant,
before you go spilling your seed all over the place! I tell you
that before there can be colored worshipers in my church,

there will have to be a great deal more spadework—lessons in how to deal with hate—*sermons*."

He was startled by Jim's saying slowly, "I could . . . almost go along with you in that. Suppose the worshipers do stay away for a while. Suppose we do forget about the janitor's job. What then?"

Seth was so startled that for a moment he was speechless. Had his own rage and suffering, or rather the explosion of the same, served to purge the atmosphere? Was this change in Jim—was it—did it represent *respect*? What had happened? And what had happened to him, because it was coming quite clear to him, the "what then," rather than any taking refuge in "Isn't that enough?" It was as if, while waiting in his study, he had planned it all out in an orderly way, which he had most assuredly not done, though he had meant to; he had never "arrived," for thinking of Old Mackie and the like.

"Well," Seth said, "there's always the Ministerial Association."

"Yes," Jim said. "It's a very influential group."

"My way would be trying to get colored ministers admitted into that. I could . . . I will introduce a motion to the Association to that effect."

"That would be an important step," Jim said.

"I'm on the hospital board," Seth said. "With the colored wing, why shouldn't colored doctors be on the staff? I'll push that."

"That would be excellent," Jim said. "A great help."

"But you," Seth said, "you must defer your test case in the courts by at least a year."

"I can't do that," Jim said.

Their eyes moved, by common accord, to Jimbo who looked up from his picture book and smiled at them. Neither man smiled back.

"Abraham and Isaac," Seth said in a low voice. "Only, as it turned out, God didn't require Isaac's charred remains of Abraham. You must defer your case." He did not pause. "This is what you must do instead—I'm chairman of the school board, you know."

"I'm not entirely unaware of that fact," Jim said.

But this sparring was below par when compared to their former bouts of cruelty.

Seth said, "For this fall, you must get up a petition, with as many signatures as you can, calling for the end of segregation in the public schools here. As the authorized representative of your organization, write a covering letter and deliver copies of the petition and the letter to the school superintendent and to me. I'll place the petition before the board at a regular monthly meeting in the course of its regular business and the board will have to at least take it under study. The letter and the petition should ask that immediate steps be taken to reorganize the public schools under our jurisdiction on a non-discriminatory basis. And it ought to conclude something like this, 'Please rest assured of our willingness to serve in any way we can to help you in dealing with this question.'"

Jim said, "And are you sure this isn't just a delaying action?"

"Nine chances out of ten, it won't work," Seth said, "if that's what you mean. But it will help to make the way of the other less rocky. And I think we do have to make a big effort to appeal to the best in people rather than waving the red flag at the worst in them. I'll help you with the other when the time comes; when and if this fails."

"Thank you," Jim said, so that Seth's eyes were suddenly smeared with tears that he had to blink away.

"How many signatures to such a petition could you get?" he asked.

Jim hesitated. "Maybe fifteen."

"Very good," Seth said. "But you'd have to make it clear to all potential signers that the minute it becomes public, they'd stand to lose their jobs and maybe worse. Some of them definitely would lose their jobs."

"They know."

"I might be able to get a white signer or two for you."

Seth stood up. Jim also got to his feet.

"There's somewhere I have to go now," Seth said.

"I hope you'll understand that I'm not meaning to be impertinent," Jim said. "But I can't help wondering . . . I feel I have to ask, as I did of someone else once before, whether . . . or rather, how much all this depends on—uh—Mrs. Hibbard's approval."

Seth looked at his watch. "There's only one way to find out," he said in a flat voice. "That's where I'm going now. I'm going to see Mrs. Hibbard."

They stood there.

Jim said, "I . . . I have to feel that you *are* forewarned. It's quite likely . . . I mean, you may . . . It . . ."

"I know," Seth said. Then he said, "I think I do know. They'll try to tear me to pieces too. We'll just have to see."

"Come on, son," Jim said to Jimbo.

Jimbo climbed down from the chair. "I hate to leave this," he said, hugging a picture book to his chest.

"Take it with you," Seth said, giving him a strange, shy smile. "It's yours now."

4

He was locking the study door when he heard those rapid, bumbling footsteps—Jesse's, Jesse Tate's—coming up behind him. He turned and met the concentrated, passionate, tender regard.

"Well, Seth?"

"I'm on my way somewhere, Jess. I'll see you later. I'll call you as soon as I can. Will that be all right?"

Jess knowing and not knowing how much Seth was counting on him as the chairman of his board of deacons, and not merely in regard to that meeting tomorrow.

He turned into Rabbit Road, bareheaded, walking slowly. Feeling that he would need the extra time it would take him walking to collect his thoughts, he had left his car at the church. On the face of it, it was ridiculous to be searching and probing for an Achilles' heel in Carrie's iron constitution. One should admit right off that in that implacable, terrifyingly efficient mortal, it was exactly that one weak and vulnerable spot that had been left out—simply and absolutely, there wasn't one! One would save oneself considerable anguish by admitting immediately that searching and probing were so much effort down the drain. And yet: what was a wasted imagination for, if it was not to serve one once?

Carrie *was* mortal, wasn't she? All men are mortal, Socrates
is a man, therefore Socrates is mortal. (Socrates drank the
hemlock.)

He directed his steps up the brick walk. Imagination or no
imagination, nothing had occurred. Carrie's car was in the
garage, Fred's was not; Fred, of course, would be at work at
Repelius'. He supposed he would have to content himself with
the reminder that he did at least know a thing or two about
Carrie's tactics. He rang the bell. After all, he and Carrie
could exchange a few comments on the weather and each
know precisely where the other stood. This was their way.
And if she was an Erwin, so was he. This was it.

She was taking an uncommonly long time to come to the
door, which stood carelessly ajar, this last bothering him a
mite, in that it hardly seemed like Carrie whose doors were
either open or shut but never lolling. And when at last he did
hear footsteps in the hall—slow and shuffling steps—his first
thought was of the cleaning woman Carrie sometimes had in,
yet immediately realizing this could not be, inasmuch as
Carrie would not hire a woman who did not pick up her feet.
Listening to these steps, a fine cold sweat broke out all over
him. *Never faster, never slower; incapable of deviation, the*
steps that had patrolled the floor of his mind for years. Like a
double take—this shuffling, broken progress. He had to force
himself to raise his eyes. Then they stood silently regarding
each other. What he saw he could not yet credit as accurate.
He could be the one seeing things. She made no move to open
the screen—finally, he did; he preceded her into the living
room, but turned to make sure she had followed and was not
still standing vacantly in the hall. He waited until she had
groped her way to the sofa, then he took a chair. It was a

desolate, desolate house, ghost-ridden. Who would have said, what imagination could have foreseen or foretold, that a pale little lightweight ghost could outhaunt a two-hundred-pounder? A very frail little ghost who, in all his short life preceding ghosthood, had never got closer than the fringes? He stole another glance at Carrie but quickly cast down his eyes. Ah, Carrie, Carrie girl. He spending himself probing for the Achilles' heel when here there was general collapse, with massiveness itself become jelly-like and unfirm, yet shriveled. Except in her pew, he had not seen her since the funeral, he reminded himself; he had not been near this house. But . . . "Make it short" was the message she had sent to him at the funeral, in more ways than one. Certainly, she had been in complete possession of all her power and all her calm. But then haunting, as he also reminded himself, was not so apt to settle in until after the formalities are concluded and the corpse turned under and, even, the grass begun to sprout. It occurred to him that his failure to look at her yesterday during the course of his sermon was not the lone exception he had thought it; he had not looked at her the other Sundays which had followed the funeral either. Being haunted was different from being in mourning, though the two could exist in terrible locked combination, he would have to gather now. Did the cat prefer its mouse alive and wriggling? Or was it that the child who is not loved is still loved some? Or was it that in her heart of hearts he represented the curse and the torment which she could not do without? Or was it that a shriveled womb, so long denied its own power of expression, screamed out its recognition when its shriveled fruit was consigned to the tomb? (There was just one letter's difference if she had pushed him so fast from the one to the other.)

What was this? She had Fred still. Wasn't Fred her prize and
the apple of her eye and the obedient and docile reincarna-
tion of a Harry Hibbard; a Harry Hibbard conquered? What
more could she ask? Was he not completely under her spell
and domination? But there, he was maybe too much so, too
broken in spirit to hold her interest; too smashed within to
do more, ever, than arrange the pieces for public approval.
Poor kid, wearing his purple shoes, singing in the choir, waiting on customers at Repelius', without so much in reserve as
a secret frown. Poor adolescent; as if adolescence was not
shock enough, he had had to see, and at very close range, his
father taking a boat out on a river; what his little brother had
done with his life, at a ball game. He would always do what
Carrie told him to do. And it was conceivable that Carrie's
argument had never been centered in Fred.

Carrie, my dinosaur, my heart, what has happened to you?
Did Fred make it so plain to you, what he witnessed at a ball
game? *How dare you mourn?* Or is it the accumulation, the
delayed reaction of being doubly haunted, and is this double-
mourning? But if you must charge up two deaths to yourself,
why isn't your answer what it ought to be: *So what?* Doesn't
it irrefutably prove the point you have been seeking to establish all along: that men (an athlete, a gossamer man in
embryo should be sufficient evidence; represent sufficient
"spread") that men can be unmanned and undone; that you
are capable of defeating any man and are, therefore, the
"man" they aren't; that men are weak, vain creatures and no
match for you and your pitted strength. Well? Where's the
triumphal march, Carrie? Let's let the trumpets sound. I
don't like this. It wasn't my sermon of yesterday, was it, that
helped to set you off? A sort of repeat (come to think of it)

of another man's decision to give away some land to someone?

Come, Carrie, my petunia. Pay attention to me. If this is
mourning, plus being haunted, the chances are that you will
recover, as you would from an illness—it is probably only
temporary. You can still run Royall Furniture Company
(though it isn't as much fun, maybe, as when your husband
was a salesman traveling for it). You are *rich*. You do have
Fred. And listen, petunia, there's always Peegram, ashiver
and atremble at the mere thought of you; ready, at this very
moment, to go up in hate again, at your bidding. And, Carrie,
don't you see? There's me. *I'm* cutting up, *I'm* being naughty,
I'm behaving abominably. What's more, I'm the same man
who's been doing the major part of your fronting for you.
Isn't that a new challenge? Why do you sit staring at the
wall, holding your hands so loose between your knees? Come,
come.

—He thought it might be the way she was sitting to the
window—the window was directly behind her—that gave him
his idea.

"Carrie," he said, his voice loud, trying to dispel this sick
silence. "Carrie."

She did look at him then. Had they been fencing, it was
that he had assumed his stance and she, tardily obedient to
his summons, hers. As if the force of habit must surely count
for something! His foil, now poised and ready for the thrust
at the valentine-heart which was painted on—decorative—a
standard part of their costumes.

"Carrie. I've come to ask you, I'm wondering. I was at the
ball game while you weren't, were you? But I imagine Fred
has given you his eyewitness account. Well, Carrie, I'm

wondering whether a memorial to Harry and Ray might not
be nice. Fitting. A memorial window, say, of leaded or
stained glass—for the new church when it's built. There
could be a small bronze plaque discreetly placed below it,
one inscribed with their names along with your name as
donor and with perhaps an apt quotation of some sort. How
does that seem to you? Wouldn't you like to—uh—put up the
money for it?"

"I'll think it over," she said.

"Fine," he said.

But as an example of her parrying, this was no good at all.
And she should have come back at once with, "In a *new*
church, might not a *new* pastor have to be consulted?" or
something yet more adroit—thrust for thrust—her thrust at his
valentine-heart. It was a chance she would never have missed
to let him know where he could head in with his desegregation sermons. He had not really aroused her. Either the old
fires were banked or else extinguished entirely. But it was just
then, quite suddenly and quite clearly, that he understood his
own power—not as it related to her present collapsed state
(which was the end-result), but as it related to its cause, to
what had brought it about, to that Achilles' heel in her which
he had been searching for, to that one small and vulnerable
spot that must never be discovered and never manipulated if
the fighter is to continue the fight, so proudly and strongly
and invincibly begun, in those same terms. He had discovered it, he had discovered it yesterday when he wasn't looking and worked a knife deep into it: *She could not get on
without him!* And he could see that this present state she was
in embraced him along with Ray and Harry and that it must
indeed have been his sermon that had served to fuse them all

suddenly together to bring her low. Not just being haunted,
not just being in delayed mourning, but being crushed by a
future she was helpless under, inasmuch as the past had now
seized the future and devoured it as no more than its just
deserts. She was utterly trussed. He could have taken his
stand favoring miscegenation or sodomy and she would still
have had to bow! She had to have him around. There did
have to be room in Peegram for them both. She could not
risk driving him out of Peegram, she could not risk driving
him to the point where *he* might retaliate by taking *his* life.
And who was *he* then? He was the son of the man her mother
had fornicated with. He was Seth the son of Zebulon the son
of Seth, proud bearer of the proud name; he was a *male*
Erwin. He was the one dainty Flora had adored, pulling the
lobes of his ears. Flesh of Carrie's flesh, blood of Carrie's
blood. He was only the one who had hurt her close to first and
hurt her worst, the boy who had led the figure with her at
the senior ball. Unlike the man she had married (though perhaps not so unlike the small fruit of that union, who could
say?), he was the very one who had always toyed with the
idea of committing suicide; flesh of her flesh, she would
always have sensed this. In her orbit, he was now the only
star that had not set and, in the stricken tragedy of life, possibly the only star there had ever been. He was the son of
the man and she was the daughter of the woman who had
made their argument upon the subject of respectability a
requirement; he stood half-brother to the one she stood
cousin to, in their comings and in their goings. He was
Zebulon-in-reverse, she Abel's regret and Flora's abomina-
tion, the ghost-son of them both. He was the man who had
helped her carry out a plan, in minutest detail, of the under-

mining of another plan, the success of that plan being
what had pushed Harry Hibbard over the brink, turning
on her and daring her and whispering, "Is it or is it not
my turn?"

What was she to demand of his board of deacons when the
best they could do was cast him out of the church—that
which she could only interpret in her books as meaning he
would either leave or kill himself. How was she to shape him
and shape the town toward shaping him if all the town could
offer in the way of punishing him and bringing him in line
was more of the same, running him out or pushing him too
far. Her weapons that had destroyed two could destroy the
third and there did not seem to be any other weapons at
hand. More: it was such a terribly explosive issue that in the
event that she could not have him leave or take his life, her
problem might be simply how to hold the town back. He
could have his way with her. In their code, he could tell her
what he required of her and she would do whatever that was
—if inattentively and brokenly and observing their code (pretending she had nothing to do with anything) only from the
long force of habit. She was—although in this depressed state
—at his service, which was also why he had been able to
arouse her, even partially, even at all. Well, except on a few
points, he was not going to ask her for active co-operation; it
was only that she must not oppose him. He had come a little
way toward finding himself during this period of her suffering; his suffering had somehow added up to a better score.
He was not quite the Seth Erwin whose manhood she feared
would melt in the first heavy rain; not quite the Seth Erwin
she had grown up with. But time enough (he hoped) for
her to find that out. He would not make her sign that petition

Jim was getting up. As to these few points he did have to
have her co-operation on.

"One small thing that bothers me," he said. "Merely catch-
ing up a few threads of course. But about that incident that
nearly came off at Ray's funeral in the church . . . was
every precaution taken?"

"Yes," she said.

"It was not known, for instance, that Andy Boyd's brother
is on the police force?"

"Is he on the force?" she said.

In imitation of herself, obedient to the habit of herself.
Yes, she was at his service. . . . Had Martha Lyerly, he wondered, ever made the mistake of writing Carrie a note about
Ray, with all the criticism of the mother that such notes
imply? Had she ever "talked" to Carrie about the child who
wasn't getting on well? Certainly, it had come close to being
a most unfortunate coincidence for her that Ray, in taking
the part of his father (which had to be so automatically
against his mother), had also happened to take Martha
Lyerly's part in all the furor over the Negro issue. And it was
interesting that Carrie should have gone to the trouble of
personally warning the schoolteacher against attending the
funeral when it was of course that very warning which would
make the teacher, given her nature, have to be there. But—
and especially since it concerned the woman he was in love
with—he was probably being too harsh, assigning to Carrie's
deliberate, conscious mind that which might have been in
hiding in a dark corner.

He said, hesitating only the fraction of a second over the
surname, "Since Jim—Jim Erwin—is back in town to stay,
I should think that Mayor Franklin, and through him certain

others, could be persuaded, through channels, to so warn
Andy Boyd, and his cohorts, and his brother, that they might
think twice before deciding to pull anything else rough. I
mean, I might feel a moral obligation to do a bit of talking
about why I found it necessary to depart from long-estab-
lished precedent and address a member of the congregation
as 'brother,' in the first place, and, in the second place, and
this is an even more radical departure from precedent, asked
him, at a funeral, to lead us in a closing prayer."

He hurried on. "I don't believe Wallace Packard has
worked out very well as janitor at the high school, has he?
I've heard nothing but complaints. I've heard he's stupid and
so lazy that he doesn't show up half the time. He was
taken on on trial, wasn't he?"

"I wouldn't know," she replied.

"Well, it does seem to me that Jim might have that job
back."

"I wouldn't have anything to do with that," she said.

"Of course not," he said, getting up. "I won't stay any
longer, Carrie, with the board of deacons meeting tomorrow
and all."

If the telephone had rung then, she would have half heard
it, maybe; she would not have heard the news, whatever the
news, the party at the other end sought to convey. But his
points would be attended to. It seemed so sad, so strange. In
his pity for her, he would have so liked to touch her shoulder
or kiss her cheek. He could not.

He had already reached the hall door when he heard her
say, "If we could have found one."

He turned. "Found what, Carrie?"

"A casket to fit him."

5

Outside, on the walk, he stopped, forgetting where he was and ought to be going. My God, my God. He wanted to turn around and go back in. He did not know how long he stood there in a semi-trance, but at last his thoughts did leave Carrie. He started envisaging Rotary luncheons, receptions, teas, trying to shake hands with people who didn't want to shake hands in the vestibule doors. Getting pointed out and stared at and snubbed. . . . Well, Seth? Well, Man of the Year? (He would be Man of the Year till August.) Oh, it was going to be a frightful mess. Even without Carrie working against him, it was going to be such an ordeal as every cell of his being would seek to turn away from. And he understood that it was still very much a question whether he was going to be able to take it. As for Elaine, since it had always been his success (his dressed-up and tricked-out failure) she worshiped, it was going to be terrible on her. But more than all else, he wondered whether there was even the slender chance it could work!

He realized somebody was watching him and forced himself to look up. William Morrison was sitting on the curbing of the vacant lot, with his baseball bat and his glove in the gutter at his feet.

"Hello," Seth said in the cold, reserved way he was never really able to throw off when he was addressing William Morrison. Nor did he ask whether a game had just ended or was about to begin or had failed to materialize. There were no other kids around.

"Going home?" William Morrison asked, standing up and then leaning over to collect his gear.

"I suppose so," Seth said. He had not planned to, but he supposed he could call Jesse Tate from there. They walked for half a block in silence.

"Rabbit Road," William Morrison said, looking up at the sign, upon which a sparrow was perched. "How's that for a name?"

"Harry Hibbard named it," Seth said. "I guess we could cut over to Front Street, if you'd like a soda or something."

"Sure," William Morrison said. "I could use a shake."

Odd, Seth thought, but he believed he could use a chocolate ice cream soda made with chocolate ice cream; he didn't think he had had one since he was ten. He looked at his watch: two o'clock. He had forgot about lunch.

They chose Lambeth's drugstore, which was on the first corner they came to. Ordinarily, it would not have been crowded at this hour, which was considered by Peegram to be betwixt and between, but business at Lambeth's was unusually brisk today. When William Morrison let the screen door slam behind them, it brought down a silence. Nobody spoke to them, several acquaintances turned away.

William Morrison said, "Let's sit at the counter. O.K.?"

They found two vacant stools together and sat down. William Morrison laid his bat across his knees, so that one end of it dug sharply into Seth's ribs. Red, Peegram High's own pitcher and a soda jerk as well, kept rubbing the counter up and down with a rag; not coming to take their orders; not looking their way.

"Hey, Red!" William Morrison bawled.

Seth winced. Red came straggling over.

"One chocolate shake here," William Morrison said. "What's for you, Dad?"

"Oh, I . . . a Coke, I guess." But then he said, "No. Give me a chocolate ice cream soda made with chocolate ice cream."

William Morrison looked at him and grinned.

After what seemed like years to Seth (and with William Morrison's bat playing a tattoo against his ribs the entire time, though William Morrison was completely oblivious of this), Red produced their orders. Very insultingly, he slid the glass with the soda in it and the paper cup with the milk shake in it along the marble counter. "You can pay now," he said.

"Keep your shirt on," William Morrison said. "We'll pay when we go. And bring me two of them *big* straws."

Red looked William Morrison over; William Morrison looked Red over. William Morrison said, "Don't throw me none of your curve balls." Red got the straws.

William Morrison swilled his milk shake loudly and Seth dealt with his soda. Under William Morrison's vigilant eye, he paid Mr. Lambeth, behind the cashier's desk, rather than Red. Seth even managed to say, "Nice day, isn't it?"

His instinct was to take the back way home, but William Morrison said he wanted to see what was playing at the Emporium, so they walked the length of Front Street, Seth nodding to friends and acquaintances, William Morrison loudly greeting his. It came to Seth, that he had renamed William Morrison in his heart; he had named him Zebulon, Zeb for short, Zebbie for his mother to call him.

When they got home, Seth spied some letters in the mailbox; he picked them out. He did not need to see the name and address in the upper left-hand corner or the Gate City postmark to tell him from whom one of these was—he knew instantly.

"Hey!" his son said. "Ain't that for me?"

"Yes," Seth said.

"I knew it," William Morrison said, taking it. "It's from Miss L."

"Yes," Seth said.

He opened the screen—he and William Morrison went in —William Morrison let the screen slam. He continued on down the hall and William Morrison came clattering along behind him.